Stress, Lies, and Vacancy:

The Self-Care Guide to Refill Your Empty Vessel

Dr. Raushannah Johnson-Verwayne

Printed in the United States of America
2019 First Edition
10 9 8 7 6 5 4 3 2 1

Subject Index:
Dr. Johnson-Verwayne, Raushannah
Title: Stress, Lies, and Vacancy: The Self-care Guide to Refill Your Empty Vessel
1. Black Women 2. Mental Health 3. Therapy 4. Stress 5. Anxiety 6. Trauma 7. Relationships

Paperback ISBN: 978-0-578-57120-1
Library of Congress Card Catalog Number: 2019914916

www.askdrrj.com
Email: info@askdrrj.com

Refills are a blessing...

"When you've been so used to achieving whatever you set your mind to, setbacks can be detrimental to your self-esteem and ultimately your vision for your life moving forward. When I met Dr. RJ, that's where I was in my life. Working a job I hated, involved in a romantic relationship that didn't serve me, feeling lost and disgusted. Her guidance and insistence on not only understanding the importance of self-care but making sure that I scheduled it into my life helped maneuver me out of a dark place and into the healthier space I now occupy. I am in a career that I love and feeling stronger than ever! Her book, *Stress Lies and Vacancy*, will help move you into a higher, more empowered version of yourself."

Shay Moore
Host, The Morning Grind, Hot 103 Jamz! KPRS-FM

"*Stress, Lies, and Vacancy* is one of the most empowering messages for women of color today. Having a keen awareness of how our emotions impact our body as we deal with life's challenges of career, family, and relationships is invaluable. Women will see themselves in one or a combination of the stories and hopefully be compelled to change or seek professional help to live healthier, more enjoyable lives. Dr. RJ shows readers how to de-stress and make self-care a priority which is a necessary conversation that we must all have so that we can encourage one another and lift up our sisters. This is definitely a guide to refer to for answers to general mental health questions and a support resource for years to come."

Dr. Angelise M. Rouse
Author of *The King Inside: Practical Advice for Young African-American Males* and *Born A Queen: Practical Advice for Young African-American Females*

"It's so important for women to recognize the causes and symptoms of stress, anxiety, trauma, and depression to literally help save lives. Dr. RJ shares her own personal experiences to let women know that no one is immune from psychological setbacks but that better and health and healing is possible and available if you just ask. After reading this book, encourage your sister to pick up a copy or purchase one for her. We're all in this stress mess together and there is strength in numbers."

Monique Walker, PMP
CEO
Epiphany Consulting Services, LLC

"There are several eye-opening and self-reflection moments that impacted me after reading *Stress, Lies, and Vacancy*. As a workaholic, I clearly see how my constant stress to meet deadlines and be everything to everyone can negatively impact my physical, mental and emotional well-being. Now that I know better, I certainly plan to do better! Thanks, Dr. RJ, this is just what the doctor ordered.

K.A. Myers
IP Professional & Business Coach

Dedication

To my ancestors—the Queens, warriors, spiritual advisors, and mothers to children who weren't your own...thank you for the relentless and powerful DNA...with your blessing, we will rest now.

Acknowledgments

Mind, body, and spirit are essential to wellness. I am thankful to God for choosing me to be a vessel. I'm humbled by His guidance and provision.

This project was surreal. When I think about my life during this time period, I'm reminded that without my biggest cheerleaders, I would not have had the strength to move forward. Lekesha, Josina, Toni, Renata, Nicole, Cynthia, Tomeisha; thank you. You brainstormed with me at ridiculous times of the night, you filled in the gaps of my waxing and waning creativity, you helped me with simple things like "what to wear" and you held me together when my life turned into a not so amusing telenovela. You were Heaven sent and I'm so grateful for all of you.

To my TOBC loves. I find solace in our bond. Your strength and your unconditional friendship give me life. Thank you.

To my husband Adrian and my children Adriana and Ryan, thank you for sharing me. It has to be tough to compete with "Dr. RJ" and her laptop, journals, crazy hours, and introverted ways. I love that you let me be me. Thank you for allowing me to be less than a Superwoman. She's overrated anyway.

To my mother Sheneal, you've made me resilient. Being a mother is definitely one of the toughest jobs ever. Thank you for giving me all that you had to give.

To my father Charles, two words, full circle. Our timing was perfect. Thank you for being you and for unknowingly helping me be authentically me.

To my sisters and sister-friends. You're my motivation to continue to promote self-care. This is for you.

To my clients, past, present, and future; each of you are absolutely amazing. Thank you for allowing me to be a part of your journey. I've learned so much from you. You're my "why".

To my consultant, Kim. At this point, you know more about me than my therapist does! Thank you for your expertise, patience, wisdom, warmth, support, and gentle but effective push. Thank you for bringing life to a spiritual assignment. I had no idea what I was supposed to do and you were sent to me at the right time. I'm so very grateful.

Author's Note:

The stories represented are not the stories of real clients and are combinations of several outcomes in various contexts to provide examples of certain patterns of behaviors. No story is representative of one actual client. Instead, they are a combination of several individuals and incidents into one person to emphasize the specific subject matter.

Foreword

The book *Stress, Lies, and Vacancy* should be a required read for all African American women coming into womanhood and it should be re-read annually to remind us all of the importance of self-preservation. *Stress, Lies, and Vacancy* makes one look at the "(wo)man in the mirror" and deal with the accurate reflection before us.

It is an enjoyable and easy read, but most importantly it is thought-provoking. When you get on the plane they always say put on your mask and then the mask of those around you that need help. The airline realizes you cannot help anyone until you sustain yourself. This book made me see clearly that I have been putting on others mask while I expose myself to danger, by not taking care of myself. It talks about a phenomenon we as black women suffer, we are often everything to everyone, while we completely neglect ourselves.

I am an admitted overachiever. I am a proud graduate of Howard University and the message that was beat into my head was that you are black and female and so for you good is not good enough, you must be great and certainly better than your white counterpart. I am a single Mom and provider for my daughters,

21 and 20-years-old, a provider for my parent, a lawyer that runs a boutique law firm where I serve professional and high profile clients and am I often a featured guest speaker. In my personal life, I date a man that is just as busy as me. It is my goal to always perform at the level of excellence. Thus, I work 6 days a week and from 8 am to 10 pm regularly. I attempt to be everything to my clients, and family while completely neglecting myself.

In my head, I know that Judges expect me not to be prepared when I come before them, and juries do not instantly give an African American female lawyer the credibility of being a great lawyer on sight, as they may do for my white male counterparts. I am always required to prove myself. *Stress, Lies, and Vacancy* gave me the permission I needed to stop, pause, and realize it is time to take time out for me or suffer the consequences. The book made it OK to get support from professional resources and OK to stop and smell the roses.

There will be sections in the book where you swear you were sitting on the doctor's couch because they nailed your experience, and those sections will be painful and enlightening at the same time. There will be other sections that are not your experience at all but the ability to experience them through the doctors clever writing will give you the perspective you need to be more compassionate to others.

Dr. R.J. was able to make an easy two hour read a life-changing experience and I highly recommend it to women from all walks of life. It is great to look altogether for the world but this book will help you to take steps to make sure that you are all together for the most important human in your life, YOU!

Fani T. Willis
The Law Offices of Fani T. Willis, LLC.

Table Of Contents

"I have come to believe that caring for myself is not self-indulgent. Caring for myself is survival."
- Audre Lorde

"Women of color must adopt a self-care mindset and vow to keep themselves healthy and whole so they can carry out God's purpose for their lives. It's impossible to do what you are called to do if you are depleted. "
- Dr. RJ

INTRODUCTION

I Am My Sister's Keeper

You're definitely worth it. Are you ready to *finally* do you? It's time to *level up*! I know it sounds cliché but this "girl power" anthem will be around for years to come. We all need to push each other to strive to do better in many areas of our lives. I'm not talking about leveling up in your career, family, or dating prospects. Of course, those areas are important, but I want to encourage you to prioritize and *level up* in your personal health and self-care mindset.

Imagine standing at a one-way crossroad—you can't turn back or to the left or right. You can only move forward. One road leads to a path with scenes from your current life as an overworked, overly-stressed, superwoman with the "red-bottoms" but *without* the red cape. The other road leads to a bright, sunny path along white sandy beaches where you engage in physical activity, eliminate avoidable stress, meditate, pray, and get a restful night's sleep. Which path do you choose? Are you leaning towards the dreadful cycle of catering to everyone's needs but yourself? Or are you feeling a renewed sense of self-worth and stroll along the sunny path? Choosing the beach path is the first step towards putting a stake in the ground to become a hands-on advocate for your emotional, mental, and physical

3

well-being. Within a short time, you will see how this is the right path for you.

For too long, Black women have spent the majority of our lives caring for others while ignoring our own personal health. We all need to take a break, refill, and recharge. When I think about how we tend to operate I envision us as a beautiful pitcher filled with water. We are at a table with at least ten empty glasses. Our superwoman instinct kicks in and sprint to the glasses and begin filling each one up to the rim, nearly overflowing. Once we catch our breath we realize that we are completely empty— actually dry and need to quench our thirst. Yet we have nothing left to give. The reality is that if you replenish yourself the next day, it will be poured back out as quickly as it came in. The cycle has to stop.

Black women have grown up with this ingrained idea that wearing a badge of self-sacrifice is honorable. Who sold us this lie? As a Licensed Clinical Psychologist, many of my clients are successful women who have taken self-sacrifice to extremes, despite their own traumatic life experiences. Often we are bearing the burdens of our entire family, with no outlet to cry, vent or ask for help. We all need to find the courage to end the cycle of dysfunction and despair by seeking therapy and making immediate alterations to our current routine.

I don't think most women of color realize that there is a direct historical link from the trauma of slavery that contributes to the overworked, black-superwoman complex. Studies have shown that there are environmental factors that can affect our genetic offspring. Since the nervous system of humans and mice are similar, in one study, mice were trained to fear the smell of orange blossoms. Each time the mice were near the orange blossoms, they were jolted with an electric shock. It's no surprise that mice offspring of up to three generations all shuttered merely at the smell of orange blossoms, even when they weren't shocked.[1] This notion of Epigenetics is real and our physical and emotional responses to an event, like the trauma of slavery, are traits that can be passed down from one generation to another.

The science is real and we are a people with an amazing history of contributions to American society and the world at large. I want to make it clear that I don't believe slavery is who we are or the end result of who we can become. It was a horrendous, tragic moment in African-American history that has had negative repercussions that need to be dealt with head-on. Specifically, it's the trauma from the events of slavery that needs to be discussed and processed to prevent bad patterns, in order to understand and process good patterns.

Refilling your empty vessel should be part of your newly learned behavior. The majority of us were never taught how to take care of ourselves. Instead, the superwoman myth has prevailed and it's time for the self-sacrifice mindset to end. Even Wonder Woman took a break from using her superpowers as nurse Diana Prince. We need to give ourselves routine breaks from our superhuman roles. Of course, I'm all for our black girl magic taking on the world but not to the detriment of our souls, health, spirit, and well-being. Our goal should be to find a balance between being amazing and shifting focus to relax and replenish.

I'm also mindful that there is a population of women who view self-care as a bad thing or a sign of weakness. They feel guilty about taking care of themselves. These are high functioning women who are doing incredible things in all areas of society, yet they do *nothing* for themselves. Self-care refuels us rather than takes from us. Practicing self-care is a sign of strength and wisdom. We should encourage and praise the mom who chooses to leave her children in daycare an extra hour so that she can work out. Physical and emotional health is a *need*. Healthy interactions with other adults is a *need*. Sleep is a *need*. It's time to reframe our wants to differentiate them from our life-sustaining needs.

This book is divided into three sections: Part I Stress deals with the effects of stress on the body, psychological perspectives, and negative emotions. Part II Lies presents lies we've bought into by the church, family secrets, and society as Black people. Finally, Part III Vacancy exposes the aftermath of the negative impact of stressors which lead to anxiety, depression, isolation, and suicidal ideation.

Self-care is my proverbial phone booth. It's my safe haven. It's how I recharge my smile and how I show gratitude to my Creator. I want readers to take away this doctor's orders to "Do You" but for the purpose of essentially helping others. I hope you find this book informative, empowering and transformational. At the end of the day, we're all in this together and we can be a powerful force in the wellness shift of Black women. We must be willing to stand in the gap and be accountable to our sisters who are struggling to make self-care a priority, ashamed to seek therapy or find it impossible to take off the cape and mask. I've been there and done that more times than I can count.

This guide is what I like to think of as the ultimate middle path to wellness. So many women feel ashamed and alone because of their experiences. However, as a psychologist I understand that self-disclosure can be a powerful and effective tool. I'm sharing my story to wellness as an illustration of how a journey can look. Every journey is different and each one just a little bit easier with a guide. I'm on a mission to do everything that I can personally and professionally to refill the empty, broken vessels of my sisters one sister at a time.

PART I

STRESS

"Heart disease is the number one
killer of black women."

*"I'm all for our black girl magic
taking on the world but not
to the detriment of our souls, health,
spirit, and well-being."*
— **Dr. RJ**

CHAPTER 1

Stress & Self-Care

What exactly is self-care? Is it caring about yourself? Caring about what you eat?

Exercising? Time management? Saying "no"? Overall, self-care is a combination of all these things. It is an intentional act to ensure that your mental, emotional, and physical health are in check. Self-care is an essential *need* for survival, not a want, so it must take priority in your life. The more you practice self-care, the sooner you'll notice that your mood and outlook are more positive because you're operating in a reduced state of anxiety and stress.

Your relationship with yourself is more important than anything else, outside of your relationship with God. Put yourself back into your rightful position in the original hierarchy with God first, then yourself. Unfortunately, for many women self-care is viewed as a foreign concept. When women have downtime and take breaks or choose themselves over something else, it is viewed negatively. This notion has always puzzled me because people are dying from stress, aneurysms, heart disease, and other stress-related illnesses because they are tired and depleted, with absolutely nothing left to give.

Think back on the analogy I mentioned earlier where Black women are beautiful filled pitchers of water at the center of her family, church, community, job, and just about everything. All of the 10 water glasses are filled to capacity. This means that she is completely empty. Women need to know the importance of refilling, stepping back from the emotional and physical overload to recharge or we will suffer health serious consequences. It is a simple, yet complex situation because we have historically taken care of everyone else, and we totally miss the part about steps to make sure that we are healthy. No one talks about the repercussions of *not* taking care of yourself, as if it were a true secret. I think if we talked about it more and if we passed it down from generation to generation, then we won't fall into the self-sacrificed stress trap as often.

Have you ever read a magazine or newspaper article about men being compared to "Superman?" I haven't. Instead, men are expected to go to work and come home— that's pretty much it. I am not man-bashing in the least, but women are expected to be "Superwoman" every day at any and all costs. I think we as women are partially to blame because we take on way too much and then become resentful for our hard work and sacrifice. I used to tell myself that I had so many things to do and I was all over the place trying to control things that were more than likely beyond my control. Quite frankly, I convinced myself that the myriad of things on my list was the least I could do, so I tried to do more. Now, if I have a choice, I choose *me* every single time.

For example, I currently have two young children which means there are birthday parties almost every weekend. I tell them, "Guys we are going to choose one birthday party each this month." Oftentimes, someone else will take them to a birthday party, because frankly, I just don't like kid's birthday parties. Does this make me a bad mom? No. I'd much rather spend my Saturday morning relaxing, working on a project, doing something around the house or lounging in the sun. Yet there are women who love birthday parties, so attending one every weekend is self-care for them. Self-care is an individual thing and you have to give yourself permission to think of yourself first. I am officially giving you permission to put *your* needs first. It's the right thing to do. It's Godly and it's spiritual. It will provide you with more clarity, energy, and joy, which puts you in a better position to clearly hear God's voice. By becoming an active listener, you can receive what He is telling you since you are not preoccupied and frazzled by a never-ending "To-Do List" for others. If you set a *me first* example now, it can have a ripple effect. Our lives depend on it. Our kids are watching us, our families are tuned in, so are our employees, friends and even strangers. Therefore, we can say to the 20-year-old, "yes you can be ambitious and have it all, but not at the expense of your emotional, mental and physical health."

Self-care versus Self-indulgence

"It's OK to treat yourself, but…"

I cannot overemphasize the importance of intentional self-care. On the flip side, not practicing self-care can actually lead

Chronic Stress & You

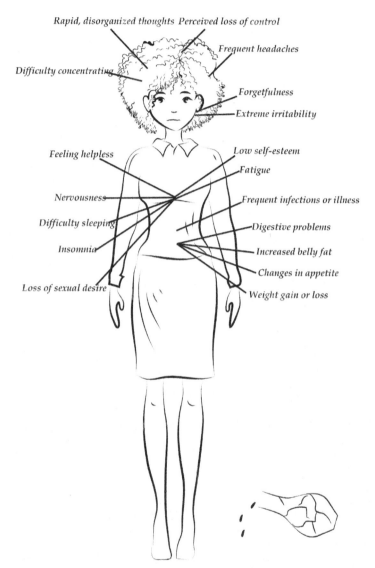

to selfishness and other negative behaviors. What tends to happen is that you deprive yourself and cater to others. Since you receive zero reciprocity, you then become this martyr in your mind. Trust me, I know because I've been there. Since you perceive that no one is there for you, you shut down and become resentful, yet feel justified in your actions. Now, as the person who was always there for others, you become selfish and withdraw from people by withholding time, affection, and love as a punishment to them because you are exhausted and depleted. On the outside looking in, it is a bizarre picture. From another perspective, not caring for yourself is a bit grandiose. Feeling like you don't need to relax, recharge or take a break is problematic. *Who do you think you are that you can keep going and going without consequences?* If we treat ourselves like robots others will learn to do the same. Whether our spouse, children, coworkers, or friends, people will learn to treat you the way you "teach" them to treat you.

On the flip side, self-indulgence is doing things solely for the purpose of pleasing yourself. There's nothing wrong with treating yourself from time to time, but it can become extreme. I co-led one of the Dave Ramsey Financial Peace Groups through my church-wide program. One great example he used was for group members to look at their bank accounts as a way to determine their priorities. If every expense in your bank account is all about you, then you need to shift a little. Self-indulgence is not necessarily a bad thing but too much of any one thing can be harmful. Balance is key.

Self-care is about being a good steward of our feelings and emotions or needs so we don't behave badly and cause problems in our personal and professional relationships. If we are on edge all the time, it creates tension all around us. Self-care is about seeking and nurturing our insecurities. When we are compassionate towards ourselves it becomes second nature to show compassion and grace to others and give ourselves a break. On the contrary, when our emotional needs are not met then we become co-dependent and latch on to someone who we believe meets our needs and they believe we meet theirs. This transpires into an unhealthy back and forth that spills over into other areas of our lives.

The good news is that there are steps that you can take to manage your stress triggers. One way is through deep breathing. We can monitor breathing simply by inhaling and exhaling several times: breathe in five seconds and breathe out five seconds. Each time you do this you are sending a signal to your brain that everything is OK. This makes your heart rate slow down, which is the assurance that you are in a normal relaxed state. Controlled and intentional breathing is easy and simple to incorporate into your day to stop the stress response from happening. Then if you want to really control it or stop it even more and change its path, begin with progressive muscle relaxation from head to toe then from toe to head. Instructions for doing progressive muscle relaxation are provided at the end of this chapter. Just think about it, if your muscles are relaxed then you cannot fight, run or freeze. This tells your body, "Check" everything is OK." Keep in mind that the process is like doing the wave at a football game. It's a constant back and forth between your brain giving signals to your body and your body sending signals back to your brain.

Practical Steps to manage your stress:

- **Listen to your body: Pay close attention to how your body responds to stressors.** Are you sleeping at night? Are you easily angered? Are you binge eating at night? Are you engaging in destructive behaviors like drug and alcohol use that is out of your norm?

- **Engage in more physical fitness activity:** Exercise and weights, walking, swimming, and biking or even Zumba.

- **Choose mindful, relaxing activities:** Meditation, yoga, Tai Chi, painting, drawing, and hobbies. Create a vision board and celebrate the little things.

- **Prioritize:** Set realistic goals for the day or for the week.

- **Seek Fellowship:** Connect with people who can provide emotional and other support such as helping out with various responsibilities or healthy distractions.

- **Contact a licensed professional therapist.**

Take Control...

"Your breathing is your greatest friend.
return to it in all your troubles and
you will find comfort and guidance."
*- **Unknown***

Progressive Muscle Relaxation

Begin by finding a comfortable position either sitting or lying down in a location where there will be no interruptions. Allow your attention to focus only on your body and your breathing. If you begin to notice your mind wandering, without judgment, bring it back to the muscle you are working on. It's perfectly okay and you can expect your mind to wander during this exercise. Gently bring your attention back to your body. Take a deep breath. Breathe in through your nose (inflate your abdomen like a balloon), hold for 2-3 seconds, then exhale slowly like deflating a balloon. As you breathe in, notice your stomach rising, and your lungs filling with air. Repeat slowly and patiently. As you breathe out imagine the tension in your body being released and flowing out of your body. And again breathe in… and breathe out. Notice the change in your heart rate and the feeling in your chest. Now tense each muscle group, one group at a time from head to toe then from toe to head. Squeeze, release, squeeze, release and repeat. As you go through each step, breathe slowly and try not to hold your breath. Notice how your muscles feel when they're tight and how they feel when they are relaxed. Become familiar with the relaxed feeling.

"It's not the load that breaks you down, it's the way you carry it."
— **Lena Horne**

CHAPTER 2

You're Not Alone

"...when i can't express
what i really feel
i practice feeling
what i can express
and none of it is equal..."

— ***Nikki Giovanni,*** *"Choices"*

W e're all in this stress mess together! Everyone has common stressors. There is good stress and bad stress. While we should embrace the good stress for the protection that it serves to our body, we must learn how to chip away at the bad stress triggers. Self-care and therapy can help you manage the inevitable stress in your daily lives. Most women are suffering in silence and are afraid to take active steps to mitigate their emotional and physical well-being. Make today your *Ah-ha* moment and reach out to someone who can help— silent suffering must no longer be an option.

Stress affects everyone regardless of age, race, culture or religion. It is a natural communication between our brain and body responding to demands. For every situation that we en-counter, there is a demand or stressor that governs our ability to deal with the incident. Whether it's our family, career, school, life changes, or trauma, all of these common events can be stressful.

In my practice, I've seen hundreds of accomplished women operating in stress overload. Many call my office in a panic to come in immediately. Quite frankly, the human side of me is saddened by those that never show up, but the therapist in me totally understands the challenges. I'll never forget Yolanda. Our brief conversation left an imprint on me because I could feel the sheer desperation in her voice.

It was one Friday evening around 6:30 as I was packing up to head home. Just when I was about to forward the phone lines to the answering service the phone rang. The ring startled me because my thoughts were on my date night plans, and I was already running late. *Should I answer it? No! Never answer the phone unless you want to handle who's on the other end. It's Friday after hours. You need to get going.* These thoughts roamed in my head. By the fourth ring, I felt compelled to answer.

"Hello, Standard of Care Psychological Services, Can I help you?"

"Yes, I'd like to speak to the doctor, Dr. RJ please." The woman on the other end sounded rushed and worried, as though she only had a few minutes to make the call or something terrible would happen to her.

"This is Dr. RJ. How can I help you?"

"This is Yolanda. I need to make an appointment right away. It's been too long. I can't take this pressure and stress anymore.

I feel like I'm going to explode. It's coming from my job, my husband, his family, the kids, and the list goes on. I'm up for a big promotion at work. I have heart palpitations and I haven't slept in months. I'm on edge with everyone all day. I can't take feeling like this and I really need to see if you can help me."

"I have an opening on Tuesday at 11:00 AM? Will that work for you?"

"Tuesday, umm I was really hoping for Monday."

"Well can you make Monday at 4:00 PM?

"Yes, I can. Great thanks so much. I'll see you on Monday."

When I hung up I was happy that I'd answered the phone. I was looking forward to meeting Yolanda on Monday. Late Monday morning, I received a message from the front desk that Yolanda called to cancel her appointment for later in the afternoon. The note said that she would call back to reschedule. After three more cancellations, Yolanda finally showed up at my office.

At first glance, she was a dead ringer for Tracee Ellis Ross. She wore a beautiful black and white houndstooth designer wrap dress and three-inch black pumps. She came across as a Type A professional as she rummaged through her black Dooney & Bourke bag searching for her lip balm. Yolanda married her college sweetheart and they have two teenagers. She was in all of the fast track executive leadership programs and before graduating landed an internship with a Fortune 100 company. Since then she has received several promotions as she comes on early and works late into the evening with little time for her family. As an executive woman of color in a high profile organization, there is constant added pressure to succeed in everything she does. Yolanda provides a great deal of financial support to her extended family and recently discovered her husband was having an affair. Her son is on drugs and she is battling with her siblings as to whether to put her mother in a nursing home. Yes, she has a lot on her plate, like many of us, and it is a great first step that she made to take charge of her life and health.

Yolanda is dealing with a lot of stress daily. It is important to pay close attention to how you deal with major and minor stress events so that when you feel overwhelmed, it is a sign that you may need to seek help. When we are stressed, our brain immediately tells our body that something serious is going on and we need to be prepared. From a physiological standpoint a few things happen quickly:

i)   your heart rate goes up;

ii) your pupils dilate;

iii) your blood sugar escalates, cortisol gets dumped into your system and peaks;

iv) all of your vital functions shut down, so your brain's frontal lobe (where all executive decisions are made) shuts off; and

v)   your brain tells your body it's a fight or flight moment.

This two-way communication is fast and ongoing, and at times may make you feel like you are on an emotional rollercoaster. The sooner you learn how to deal with your stressors the more relaxed and productive you will feel in the long-run. It's great that our bodies have a shutdown mechanism to protect us from danger, yet imagine the consequences of the long-term damage your constant stress mode signals are sending to your body when there is no imminent danger? It's time to manage your stress once and for all.

Code You

As we just learned, every time there is a perceived stressor your brain instantly goes into an active cycle of transmitting information to your body. Once the stressor goes away, you return to a calm state. For some of us, stress triggers happen occasionally. For others, maybe a few times each week. Yet for many of you, stress triggers are operating in chronic stress mode, so you never get to experience that calm state. You've probably been functioning at chronic stress levels for so long that you don't even realize it—it's your normal. Therefore, not only is your body undergoing physiological changes, you are now more susceptible to physical ailments like diabetes, high blood pressure, obesity, insomnia, irritable bowel syndrome, anxiety and depression—all because you are *unknowingly* triggering a constant panic attack. It's all systems go as you live in emergency mode and your body is telling you to run, fight or hide. Keep in mind that negative stressors can also harm your baby if you are pregnant, wreak havoc on hormones, make acne worse, cause your digestive system to go haywire, and lead to heart damage. We have to take stress seriously because of the major damage it does when left untreated.

"*My life has been filled with terrible misfortune; most of which never happened.*"
— ***Michel de Montaigne***

Another negative impact of stress on our body is forgetfulness. Since all communications to our frontal lobe are cut off we appear scatterbrained. We constantly lose things, pass our exit on the highway, or search for our glasses on our foreheads. Does this sound familiar? Chronic stress blocks the body from producing insulin which lets glucose (sugar) pile up in the blood. As sleep decreases, blood sugar increases and the body tries to get rid of the extra sugar through the kidneys—which means waking up in the middle of the night to go to the restroom. It's a vicious cycle. This leads to insomnia which increases irritability. Just think about it, if you don't sleep or have poor sleep patterns, then that's another issue that interferes with your daily functioning and can be very dangerous.

It's hard to believe that this quote is over five hundred years old and is credited to the French philosopher, Michel de Montaigne. How many times have you worried about things that never happened? I can honestly say that I've done this more times than I care to count. A few years ago, a study by Clinical Psychology & Psychotherapy demonstrated the accuracy of this quote. As part of the study, participants were asked to write down their worries over a specified time and then write down the outcome of all of the events. Would you believe that 85% of what the participants worried about never happened! Turns out, the remaining 15% who experienced the event realized that they could handle it without the traumatic effects originally believed, and a majority of them learned a lesson from the experience.[2] As you can see, most of our stress is nothing more than imaginary thinking that you know what someone is going to say or do and then internalizing a negative outcome for the day, week, month or years to come. It's time to stop beating yourself up prematurely about how something or someone is going to affect you in the future. You're stronger than you realize and capable of facing your fear head-on in victory.

Don't be discouraged because there's good news. Despite all of the negative impacts of stress, you have the power to fix it! The brain has neuroplasticity which means that it can be re-trained and reprogrammed. Chronic stress can change the brain structurally and functionally, yet therapy and treatment can also change the brain in the same manner. Therefore, the negative impacts of stress on our physical and emotional health can be reversed over time and lead to a healthier lifestyle.

Myelin Matters

Today, chronic stress has become so normalized to the point that those suffering from chronic stress have no idea they are experiencing stress nor the toll it is taking on their mental and physical health. Chronic stress is our body's response to pro-longed emotional pressures to the point where we resolve in our minds, "*Oh well, it is what it is!*" Feelings of hopelessness in your situation, when left untreated, is dangerous. Are you currently responding to chronic stressors? Have you recently lost a loved one? Been laid off? Lost your home? In an abusive relationship? If you answered "yes" to any of these questions you may be impacted by chronic stress.

When you are constantly stressed a white substance or mat-ter is produced on the brain that hardens called myelin. It is a protective sheath-like material in your central nervous system that transmits electrical impulses quickly to perform a task. Cortisol increases myelin and over time when the white matter hardens like glue wrapped around neurons, you become less efficient at thinking and problem-solving. Myelin can be good or bad depending on the time or the place in the brain. The hippocampus which regulates memory and emotions actually shrinks under extended periods of acute stress. The hippocampus plays a pertinent role in disorders like depression, PTSD, or suicide.

As myelin covers the brain it interferes with our neural pathways, the place where new learnings and retrieving old memories occur. The catch-22 is that we make it worse and increase stressors with seemingly harmless behavioral messages like, "Oh my goodness, why can't I remember these things? Why can't I figure this problem out?" These messages increase physiological stress and it's like playing ping pong with the brain and body stress responses. This mind-body danger game has to stop somewhere and intervention is the short answer. When this happens, you can stop and begin a deep breathing exercise. This would be a complete behavioral change. Cognitive behavioral therapy will help turn those negative cognitions: thoughts, feelings, behaviors, and reduce your stressors and ultimately change your cognitions. Although it's easier said than done, I encourage you to eliminate unnecessary stress in your life and only focus on things that you can control and change. Take the stress test on the next page to t give you a snapshot of your current stress level.

How Stressed Are You?

<u>Please note:</u> This scale is not a clinical diagnostic instrument and is provided for self-awareness only. It merely identifies some of the symptoms of stress that you may be unaware of. If you have any concerns about the results please contact your primary care physician or therapist.

0) Never 1) Sometimes 2) Often 3) Always

1. I feel tired - _____
2. I use caffeine or nicotine - _____
3. I have sleep problems (i.e. falling asleep, staying asleep, or restless sleep) - _____
4. I get headaches - _____
5. I have stomach issues (i.e. nausea, vomiting, diarrhea, constipation, gas, irritable bowel) - _____
6. I find it hard to make decisions - _____
7. I forget little things (i.e. where I put my keys, details from work meetings, names) - _____
8. I find it hard to concentrate - _____
9. I am irritable and easily annoyed - _____
10. I have back or neck pain/stiffness/discomfort - _____
11. I have mood swings or feel overly emotional - _____
12. I eat too much or too little - _____
13. I feel overwhelmed and helpless - _____
14. I find it hard to relax or wind down - _____
15. My work performance has declined and/or I have trouble completing things - _____

Score:

0-11 Keep up the good work. It looks like you don't sweat the small stuff

12-23 Be careful. Little things are starting to add up.

24-35 Warning; a score in this range suggests you may be experiencing a moderate to high level of stress

36-45 It's time to make some immediate changes. This score suggests that you're in the danger zone.

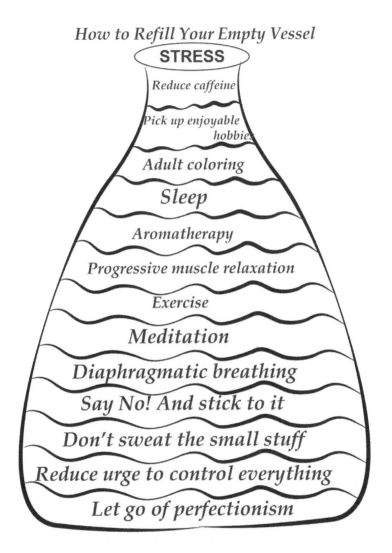

How to Refill Your Empty Vessel

STRESS

Reduce caffeine

Pick up enjoyable hobbies

Adult coloring

Sleep

Aromatherapy

Progressive muscle relaxation

Exercise

Meditation

Diaphragmatic breathing

Say No! And stick to it

Don't sweat the small stuff

Reduce urge to control everything

Let go of perfectionism

"*In every crisis, there is a message. Crises are nature's way of forcing change—breaking down old structures, shaking loose negative habits so that something new and better can take place.*"
— **Susan L. Taylor**

CHAPTER 3

Mirror Mirror

ntil now, I lived more than half of my life in a negative stress cycle. Smiling and happy on the outside, yet angry at a myriad of things on the inside. I wanted a real change. I felt that after all I had been through, I *deserved* a change of pace. At the time, I welcomed the opportunity to talk with a therapist to help me identify and deal with my past and current stress triggers. Early in my practice, I found that many people were not transparent in therapy. I realized that transparency was paramount to my healing and growth process, so I was willing to be an open book.

Once I truly opened up and released everything that literally gave me heart palpitations at the mere thought of them, I became more confident and self-aware. It was so liberating. I'm not ashamed, embarrassed, nor do I have any qualms about using my personal therapeutic journey as an example of an educated, successful black woman, married with children, and learning how to handle stress one day at a time. I think what's more important is that I am committed to helping others do the same.

In graduate school, I knew nothing about stress and the toll it had taken on me prior to my arrival. In hindsight, I had no idea that I grew up in an environment where chronic stress and hardship were the norms. I never thought in a million years that *I* would need therapy. Why would I spend my hard-earned money talking to someone? Especially since I'd gotten used to talking to myself and most of the time I agreed with my own perspective and advice. Back then, I thought therapy was a luxury; something that white people did when they could not get their way. *Me? In therapy? No way!* Apparently God had different plans.

Growing up the constant theme was to survive. It was the only mindset that I knew. Not only was the theme to survive but the nickname for my city was "Bad News." How ironic. I was surrounded by struggle and engulfed by hopelessness and mediocrity. Much of this pervasive mediocrity crept into my home and permeated our atmosphere. My mother worked a lot and this left me at the mercy of a sibling who constantly reminded me that I "wasn't better than her." The more I achieved, the louder the voices became, literally. Although my mother was uplifting and encouraging, somehow it wasn't loud enough to mute the constant desire of some family members to put me in my place and keep me there. Although no one ever talked about stress in my environment, I now realize that everyone was impacted by it. There were a lot of physical and mental health problems because doctors or medicine weren't fully trusted, so they suffered which made things worse.

As a teenager, I was an excellent student but unhappy on the inside and my stomach was constantly in knots. I could not articulate what I knew about stress so it found a comfortable place in my mind and body. I kept a lot of things inside so by the time I was in graduate school I needed to purge issues from my childhood, teenage and college years. At home, the unspoken motto was, "Do well, but figure it out on your own," so I left home at 18 and went to North Carolina A&T State University.

Within the first few weeks on campus, I quickly learned that stress was normal and studying and staying up late was part of the culture of doing well and making good grades. I felt excitement and adrenaline rushes when I completed all-nighters. I was eager to go to college because my sister went first and I wanted to follow in her footsteps. I can't help but think about the grace that was afforded to me. Thanks to my praying grandmother, my undergraduate experience was fun and successful. I participated in all kinds of road trips and risk-taking, but God covered me. I'm especially grateful that smartphones and social media were practically nonexistent.

I knew I wanted to pursue graduate school and my faculty advisors at A&T became like family and pointed me in the right direction. Early on, I had a desire to become a psychologist. It was a spiritual gift that I had to walk into and felt confident that I could do the work. I was accepted into graduate school at the Georgia Professional School of Psychology in Atlanta. I was looking forward to working alongside actual people in the field as I had been a critical consumer of psychological literature and felt comfortable following scientific models.

Nothing could have prepared me for the extreme stress level of graduate school. I believe the majority of the stress stemmed from an academic system designed so that people could fail. There were close to 100 cohorts when we started and upon completion, there were less than 30—only the cream of the crop rose to the top. The graduate school environment was a culture shock. Coming from a nurturing HBCU background, I had to learn how to survive and encourage myself. To sum things up, there was a wealth of microaggressions with a sprinkle of other Black students. Of my few Black cohorts, none were from impoverished homes, so my outlook was very different from theirs. I don't think I had a night of restful sleep for at least four years.

In graduate school, I had to earn my keep so I worked full-time hours and kept a full course load. As the residential facility counselor, I worked from 11:00 PM until 7:00 AM and then went directly to class at 8:00 AM. I stole naps at work here and there but never a full sleep. It was a grind, but I was determined to finish. I had to pay my own bills and with no savings or money from my parents, I had to survive by any means necessary. Besides, I was motivated each month to stay the course as I watched people who started with me leave the program. I convinced myself that I was not going to be a casualty, therefore, I was determined not to miss a beat by falling behind or sleeping on my goal.

During the fourth year of graduate school, as a requirement of the program I had to participate in a "match" where graduate students apply to hospitals for hands-on experience. After grueling applications and interviews, if they believe you are a good match, you are invited for an internship/residency or clinic. I matched within my top three choices and interned at Sagamore Children's Psychiatric Hospital on Long Island, New York. My boyfriend, who is now my husband, was from the Bronx, so I was fortunate to have support from his parents who lived in the Bronx at the time. A prerequisite to the internship program was that as interns, we're expected to be in therapy. My first therapist was a white Jewish male. *What else could I expect on Long Island?* He was wonderful. My goal for the entire year was to clear my mind for a full three minutes. When he first said that to me, I looked at him like he was crazy. I thought to myself, *I'm paying out-of-pocket for this?* Well, in all honesty, it took me an entire year once a week to relax and clear my mind for three minutes.

During that year, I learned more about stress, relaxation, and having control of my thoughts than I had learned in my entire life. Even though I did not master it, I could see light at the end of the tunnel. My therapist uncovered "daddy issues" that I didn't realize were weighing me down. We have so much is going on in our minds that we are not aware of, yet it keeps us from enjoying the moment. In all, I learned a great deal about myself and wouldn't trade my stressful, challenging, graduate experience for more comfortable surroundings. Except for gaining 15 pounds due to my poor eating and sleeping habits, it was well worth it. I was still evolving and handling my stress levels with the help of my prescription for Xanax.

"You may not control all the events that happen to you, but you can decide not to be reduced by them."
— **Dr. Maya Angelou**

"Twinning" a Self-reflection

Have you ever gone somewhere and encountered a complete stranger that reminded you of yourself? If you answered "yes," how did you handle it? Did you like the person's reflection of you? Did you introduce yourself? Could you see yourself hanging out with the other you? Well, my close encounter with "me" happened at a conference. When I saw her, I stopped dead in my tracks. As she entered the room she was a clear reflection of my old self. It was uncanny. She was totally on edge, organized, and well put together. Definitely Type A, but in an unhappy way. I remember being exactly like her. I had these expectations and an external locus of control; wanting to control other people and being stressed and angry for days because things didn't go the way they were planned.

I know exactly where those feelings came from after years of good therapy. Some of it came from a lack of a father figure growing up as my parents were young when I was conceived. I had an inner issue with needing to control and wanting reliability. I attempted to control what I could as a child. As an adult, I made an inner vow to myself that I would no longer allow things to be chaotic and out of my control. My therapist told me that and it was a true awakening moment. Not only did graduate school give me the foundation of what I needed to be a successful psychologist, but going to therapy really helped me to better serve my clients.

I recall my final appointment with my client Leslie who had been coming to my office for two years. She was the epitome of a Type A corporate leader. Not only can I personally relate to many of my clients, but I can also offer medical, psychological, scientific, and first-hand experiences in dealing with some of their challenges. As I mentioned, until I went to therapy I had no idea why I had an insatiable desire to control everything. Part of my control issues was the result of a lack of trust in adults, fear of abandonment, and fear of losing control. Like Leslie, I took it upon myself to ensure that I controlled every environment and those in it, and was never at the mercy of anyone else. The truth of the matter is that for so many years I never thought I was controlling at all. Instead, I reasoned that I was the only one that was *right*.

Controllers are perfectionists and take on many tasks because they believe they are the only ones who can do it right. Not only do they try to control situations and others, but it also permeates into their existence and they actually control themselves by being neat freaks, workaholics, and a carb-counting and exercise fanatic. When controllers are to the extreme, they are defined as having Obsessive-Compulsive Disorder (OCD) where they have strict rules and lists for everything. I know people joke about being OCD all the time but it is a serious mental illness that is identified by debilitating levels of stress and anxiety.

A few common themes related to control issues are:

- Traumatic life experiences
- Lack of trust
- Fear and anxiety

- Low self-esteem

- Fear of failure; perfectionism

Can you relate to one or several of these themes? If so, speak with your primary care physician and ask for therapist recommendations. Therapy is not a one-hit-wonder experience. You may have to meet with a few to find the right connection. It takes time and a committed effort to make changes. I helped Leslie unpack the source for her need to control. We addressed all of her underlying fears and anxiety and developed coping strategies. Through it all, when Leslie increased her self-awareness to these issues she was able to move forward and have less anxiety about adding her dose of perfection to every situation.

Motherhood

In November 2006, I finished my dissertation and became Dr. Johnson. It was a huge accomplishment for me. I still remember it like it was yesterday. I moved back home to Atlanta and started to work on my licensure and found out I was pregnant. I wasn't sure what was going on because prior to my pregnancy realization, I found it hard to study and concentrate. The thoughts of being a new mom instantly took me back to the old RJ who needed to control *everything*. I made vows about the experiences that my unborn child would and would not have. Everything had to be the total opposite of my childhood. I kept telling myself stories like, "Nope my daughter will not be 23 years old living in my basement writing her name on the

OJ. No, not my child!" The rematch between me, myself, and I resumed.

I spent most of my 30's trying to prevent my mother's un-resolved trauma from permeating my being. I also had my own past issues that were navigating my current situation. I was a mess. The nursery had to be perfect and in order. My insatiable levels of control kept me from enjoying it all. I was so anxious and worried that something was going to go wrong. I knew if I didn't change my behavior my stress or anxiety could be passed on to her. That was a wake-up call. I'm glad those days are over yet I am reminded of them when I pull out my daughter's nursing logs and my journals during my pregnancy. Being a new mom changed me completely. I was working full-time and there were other challenges that sent me back to therapy again. I val-ue therapy and wish more African-Americans seek treatment for the common issues that affect us all. There is nothing wrong with seeking outside help and the stigma of being embarrassed or "telling your business to a stranger" is misplaced. Therapy helps and it can save lives and relationships. I've been to various forms of therapy —individual, couples, marriage retreats, and they all contributed to repairing my shattered vessel.

Four years later, I became pregnant with my son Ryan. It's hard to explain but Ryan saved me from being a current control freak. I remember the terrible mental place I was in with my daughter and I am thankful that I never have to go back there. Ryan's presence required me to be flexible and not so rigid and structured. His temperament is unpredictable and as a boy he was so different from my daughter. I had to figure out how to be OK with not knowing what's next. Ryan is a wild-card, similar to me in some ways so I have to remain flexible and be able to meet him where he is which requires calmness and stability.

My kids have a pretty healthy view of family. They talk to their cousins all the time and they are both mature for their age. My daughter Andy is compassionate and likes to help people any way she can. Andy and I had the pleasure of joining my best friend Alexis from childhood when we visited London. Alexis grew up across the street from me in Virginia and she is originally from Australia. She now lives in London with her family. My son Ryan has a kind heart and is really into helping homeless people. He volunteers often for various drives to provide food, clothing, and other necessities. Neither of my kids is into material things and they don't get a lot of toys for Christmas. I'm blessed that my wonderful husband Adriene makes our house a home as an amazing father. Although Adriene and I were raised with different upbringings: he grew up in a two-parent household and I grew up in a single-parent household, we have the same parenting goals. We may be on different pages at times, but we are operating from the same book, and our views often compliment each other. As many of you know, being a wife, mom, and business owner have its ebbs and flows so a self-care regimen is necessary to keep our minds and bodies healthy, strong and resilient.

"How simple a thing it seems to me that to know our-selves as we are, we must know our mother's names."
— **Alice Walker**

CHAPTER 4

Family Portrait

F
amily means something different to each one of us.
Whether we are speaking of an immediate family unit
consisting of parents and children living in the same
household, extended family of aunts, uncles and cousins, third
parties that we love not related by blood, or combinations of
relational connections that shape how we view and treat one
another; family is what you make it. Bishop Desmond Tutu
once stated, "You don't choose your family. They are God's
gift to you as you are to them." Therefore, we have to accept
our family members for who they are, nothing more, nothing
less.

I think we all have family challenges that unconsciously
hold us back. Most of us walk around with this invisible, yet
weighty emotional baggage carrying a backpack of issues that
stem from our childhood. As we get older and deal with life's
challenges we come to the realization that our early baggage has
taken up so much space and negatively affects our mind and
body. We learn how to deal with things from past experiences
which is normal behavior. The issues arise when we make a

brushstroke of every similar experience when we were a child and put it into the same category and outcome as adults. Since we never learned adequate coping mechanisms as a child, our interpersonal relationships bring about the heaviest emotional baggage that we carry along from one situation to the next. Some of the most common family emotional baggage patterns are i) unresolved emotional trauma, ii) never happy or satisfied; and iii) poor relationships.

Unresolved emotional trauma can keep us stuck in the same position for years. The older we get the harder it is for us to change and take on new life experiences. Traumatic events can include witnessing destruction or any violent event, as well as being directly involved in the incident such as car accident, abandonment, assault, rape, molestation, or poverty. I actually went to therapy to help bring closure to my emotional trauma. Although it was difficult to open up about my impoverished and dysfunctional family, I am glad that I did. It is such a relief to be operating in a different emotional space when it comes to family.

One of the things that stood out to me and I want to make others aware of is that if your entire family is impacted by any tragic or violent events, each one will deal with them differently. More often than not, one family member does not understand another's experience or perspective. Your sister may want to talk about it. Your mom may want to forget it ever happened. These types of behaviors by one or more members lead to misunderstandings, clashes, anger, animosity, and bitterness that pierces the relationship and creates a heap of unresolved emotional baggage for everyone involved. We'll talk more about trauma heredity in the latter chapters as such unresolved adult emotional trauma can be passed down to the children in the same household. We have to be mindful that everyone's healing and recovery take place in their own time and not ours. How many times have you thought about an incident that involved your mom or sister and said to yourself, *I can't believe she did that after all we've been through! How can she stay with him? She's definitely crazy! I want no parts of any of them!*

Anyone who has experienced a traumatic event is usually on high alert and always looking to see if something bad will happen. It is difficult for them to let their guard down. Other reactions are feeling anxious or stressed, feeling exhausted or becoming emotionally upset at the mention of the past event. Unresolved emotional trauma also rears its head in excessive behaviors like overspending (shopaholic); drinking too much, eating too much, and angry outbursts. Set your plans in motion to become emotionally free and healthy. You are already physically and emotionally drained so taking active steps now will allow you to be fluid and open to engaging in new experiences to change your perspective. Of course, I recommend therapy. However, if you choose not to see a therapist, then step outside of your comfort zone and engage in new activities or hobbies which may begin to take your mind off the traumatic event.

*"I got so focused on the difficulty of the climb that I lost sight of being grateful for simply **having** a mountain to climb."*

—Oprah Winfrey

I know you can think of a family member or close friend who is never happy nor satisfied. No matter how many things they check off their bucket list, there are still moments of unhappiness that tend to become their problem *and* your problem. The more you try to help them in areas they asked, the less appreciation you receive. You keep doing favor after favor. To add insult to injury, they give off this vibe that you could be doing more! What makes a person behave like this? Are they narcissists? They believe the world revolves around them and only them. Are they pessimists? They see the glass as half empty. Are they just ungrateful and have no rooted emotion of gratitude? It could be a combination of these characteristics or the result of the brain's physiology or their DNA.

In *Hardwiring Happiness*, neuropsychologist, Rick Hanson discusses how the brain is great with recording our negative experiences: play with fire and get burned. However, he points out that "the brain is relatively poor at turning positive experiences into emotional learning neural structure."[3] This means that when you don't actively or consciously acknowledge the good, the negative outweighs the good and always takes precedence. Think about it, you probably can recall five negative things that happened over the years and find it hard to remember one good thing last month.

Did you know that attitudes *may* be part of our DNA? Researchers have focused on optimism and self-esteem by analyzing the saliva in the oxytocin receptor gene of over 320 participants to determine the genetic influence of these personality traits. Although the results were favorable, and we have a "self-esteem gene" other experts caution that genetic variables can be skewed based on how you were raised and your life experiences.[4] Regardless of this outcome, as we discussed earlier, we can reprogram our brain to remember the good by doing many of the stress-relieving activities mentioned. Don't be too quick to judge or be angry at a family member or close friend for appearing dissatisfied with their life— positive events and outcomes need to be re-wired into their brains. We truly can accentuate the positive and eliminate the negative.

My final comment on emotional baggage deals with poor relationships. Again, not just with family, but in all interpersonal relationships. When I think about this subject matter, not only do I think about the poverty in my family, I am also mindful of the psychological impact poverty plays in any family. I understand the disruption and dysfunction it causes as a whole. In households where the adults have limited education, limited job opportunities, and limited resources, there is likely to be a wide range of unhealthy family functions. For example, older siblings raising other siblings albeit they are all children, family stress caused by lack of resources, communication, and control over the household roles and behaviors. There are times when I deal with family issues I have to ask myself, *RJ who is going to show up today? The 14-year old you (angry, violent, slick with words) or the current you who has been granted new mercy every single day? The current you who has been granted grace and favor over and over again. Will the virtuous woman show up? Or will the sad and confused little girl show up?* Every day I'm growing and when I fail, I try again. For those of you carrying the emotional baggage of your family, consider family therapy and counseling. Even if your story is as tragic as many of the families on *Iyanla Fix My Life*, there is always hope for healing, happiness, and emotional well-being.

Dear Mama

When we are going through something we believe that no one understands us. It's human nature to want to be heard and understood, especially when we are talking about the mother-daughter relationship. In a Madamenoire article titled, "The Strained Relationships Between Black Mothers and Their Daughters,"[5] Arah Ilobugichukwu nailed so many points that resonated with me and I imagine most, if not all of us. It is definitely worth reading and the link is provided in the References. She speaks about her mother's three roles as a provider, enforcer—to keep Arah from being fast, and of the hierarchy in the relationship— we are *not* friends! Does this sound familiar? After sharing stories with other women, she realized that her mother's "secretive, temperamental, and unapologetic tough love" was quite common in our community. She questions why we condone severe whippings and justify the same abuses to our daughters because we're still here. More important, both Arah and her sister developed trust issues and challenges forming relationships with women because her mother warned her not to have too many women in her circle. This is where most of our mothers got it wrong; we need a strong, safe, nurturing sister circle is necessary for our well-being. We all agree that is was tough for our mothers growing up and it is equally tough for single mothers today. However, at some point there has to be a level of accountability and resolution as we can no longer just buy into the stereotypes of raising Black girls and the old rhetoric.

"*I know my mother loves me. Not because she was the most loving, affectionate mother in the world or because she was fluent in all five love languages. But mainly because I choose to believe that everything my mother did she did out of love, even the things that didn't feel too much like love.*"

*— **Arah Ilobugichukwu***

It wasn't until I became a doctor that I truly understood the clashing relationship I had with my mother most of my life. It took me a while to be able to commit to this section of the book. My mom and I were very close during college and graduate school. I talked to her almost every day. I thought she was a superwoman. At this point in my life, I find myself in constant conflict with how I feel about my mother. I don't want to come off as judgmental but I also don't think it will help anyone if I censor myself. I vacillate between extending grace and my belief that the primary problem with our community is that we don't hold our families accountable and we don't demand that they do better. We accept the predators, abusers, criminals, discouragers, and dream crushers all in the name of family.

The 'psychologist me' knows that there should be an "and." Meaning, we should extend grace AND demand better from our families. My earliest memory of my mother is her beauty and strength. I remember thinking that she was a superwoman. She was active in the community and my love for grassroots activism stems from her. I remember wearing a white styrofoam Democratic Party hat when she campaigned for Michael Dukakis. I loved that hat. I kept thinking that it would taste like popcorn—so of course, I took a bite out of the rim of the hat which tasted bland and landed me a whipping. I'm still not sure what the whipping was for but there was no "parental debriefing" during my upbringing.

My mother tells a story about when I was 5 years old, I came home and told her that she was not allowed to spank me because it was child abuse—apparently I learned about child abuse that day in school. Well, the story is that she packed some of my belongings in a paper bag and told me that I could leave if I didn't like the way she parented. So as a five year old, I grabbed the paper bag and walked out the door. I don't remember any of this so I have no idea where I was going. We lived in a housing project called Pine Chapel which was originally military housing in Hampton, Virginia. I vividly remember the fall-out shelters at every corner. My mother said that she didn't think I would leave so when I walked out the door she had no idea what to do. She described me as "switching my tail" down the street with my head held high. Even at five, I was fearless—my relentless DNA was at work. When I got to the corner, she yelled for me to come back. Ironically, I got a "beating" for leaving the house.

When my mother tells this story, as twisted as it is, I feel a sense of pride. Early on, I learned that my mother would not know what to do with me. I often challenged her in ways that my siblings weren't allowed to. She was liberal with me. She frequently told me how beautiful and amazing I was and that I could do whatever I put my mind to doing. She never ever discouraged me. I remember after a long day at work, she found the time to entertain me. There was one time I wanted to put on a fashion show for her—on a school night in the middle of the work week. She sat down and watched me model all kinds of clothes and shoes from her closet and seemed to genuinely enjoy it.

My confusion back then was that mother was two different people. She was violent with her words, judgemental, and paranoid. Then she could shift and be gentle, attentive, warm, and engaging. My childhood memories of her are fond. I think my fairytale view ended when I had my first child. Now that I have two children, there are things about my childhood that seem unimaginable. There was poverty, turmoil, and chronic instability.

In therapy, we explored issues about my mother that I didn't know existed. My goal was to accept her for who she is and who she will never be. I also had to forgive her and just let go of this life raft that I was holding on to for survival. I was taking my childhood survival skills into adulthood survival skills where they were not needed. Yet when you grow up in that type of emotional trauma, everything seems like a war zone and you treat everything like a war zone. I count my experiences as a blessing. Now that I am on the other side of it I can identify a trigger and stop it before it takes root. I can speak to it and denounce it which gives me a level of insight and human connection which is the spiritual part of therapy. Ongoing therapy is really the conduit of change. Since I've been there and back a few times, I can definitely say that therapy works no matter how big or small your issues.

I realize now that my mom didn't have the tools or the emotional maturity during that time. I have no regrets. Every instance of my life toughened me up and prepared me for life's uncertainties. My mom instilled the confidence that I needed and she encouraged my oppositional worldview. She protected me and built up my ego. She valued education and encouraged education and breaking down barriers. She did all of this in spite of her inner pain and unresolved trauma. I am grateful that she was enough. She was just what I needed for me to be who I am, and I'm very happy with who I turned out to be. Thanks mom.

GENOGRAMS

Do the Gram

I believe that each generation should do better than the last. Self-awareness and uncovering family history are key factors. I certainly hope that my children are one hundred times better than me. Have you ever really thought about your behaviors and characteristics on a deeper level? Tracing our ancestral roots has become a billion dollar business with the popularity of companies like Ancestry.com and 23andme.com. More and more people are concerned about their DNA. Your DNA is a component of your chromosomes that carry genetic information about you. It's the science that can pinpoint family traits from generation to generation. Identifying your ancestors by tracing your roots provides key information in the creation of your family tree. Most of us are familiar with a family tree but many have not heard of genograms. Genograms are similar to a family tree, however, they go deeper into family relationships and interactions, than just direct lineage in tree branches. They are also structured more linear than a family tree. I often ask my clients to consider three things about their family that they want to keep and three things that they want to discard. Sometimes our focus becomes so narrow and we want to rid ourselves of everything that was connected to us but those connections can hold the clues to your healing and wellness.

Therapists, doctors and individuals use genograms to help pinpoint genetic predispositions to unhealthy behaviors such as alcoholism, drug addiction, and mental health issues. And yes, it also demonstrates positive traits as well. Genograms are fairly easy to create and I use them often to demonstrate positive and negative patterns to help my clients see a direct link to the majority of their challenges. You can also find more information about genograms in the Resource Pages at the end of this book as well as links with templates to create your own genogram.

Family Photoshop

Deep down, I think we all long for a picture-perfect family. Is there such a thing? It's not possible, no one is perfect and the majority of our flaws is hidden. Yet somewhere in our psyche we have bought into this make-believe image by the media of what a family is supposed to look like: two happy parents, two well-adjusted kids, two cars, a dog, and a nice home. The family unity and dynamic is changing. More women are working outside the home and there are more Black single moms functioning as head of households. A recent study demonstrated that 74.3 percent of all White children under 18 live with both parents, compared to only 38.7 percent of African-American minors.[6]

If you pull back the curtains, there are dysfunctional norms that lend itself to the reality that many marriages end in divorce. Regardless of high statistical data on divorce rates, it's important to note that divorce is not the end all. Many families are functioning at healthy levels after divorce. Parents have assumed their roles and responsibilities despite living in separate households and children have adjusted to their new circumstances.

The traditional nuclear family unit has definitely changed since our grandparents married. More and more households consists of blended families, cohabitating adults, and other family members living under one roof. In some cases, these types of living arrangements has created instability in the lives of the children residing in them because of the constant change. Children need stability to thrive and they derive that stability through safe, healthy and nurturing relationships with their parents and caregivers. In a study by the Urban Institute, by the time children are in the fourth grade, one-third of them will be on the receiving end of an unstable home environment due to divorce, re-marriage or cohabitation.[7] the beginning or ending of a cohabiting relationship. This often means changing schools and making new friends. Thus, the idea of picture perfect family does not exist. Family has so many different meanings to each of us and conjures up varied emotions that in essence, family is truly what you make it.

"The success of every woman should be the inspiration to another. We should raise each other up. Make sure you are very courageous: be strong, be extremely kind, and above all be humble."
— Serena Williams

CHAPTER 5

Sisterhood

Today more than ever, women need the love, support, and understanding of other women. Sisterhood builds deep emotional connections and is both empowering and liberating. I have a strong sister circle and I have three biological sisters to lift me up when I need it most. There are health benefits in engaging in routine interactions with female friends through sharing common bonds. Make "Girls Night" and "Girls Trips" a priority in your schedule so you that you always have something positive, fun, and exciting to look forward to.

Sister Circle

My friends, real friends, better than your friends...

No foes, real friends, we ain't even got to pretend...

Gon' pull me up, pull me up, pull me up

And never let me down (they never let me down)...

— *The Carters*

I cannot overemphasize the fact that women need other women. It breaks my heart how some women mistreat each other. Most women usually lash out against their sister because they are projecting all of their insecurities: fear, jealousy, anxiety, resentment, and low self-esteem. Oftentimes the ill-treatment stems from a strained relationship between mothers and daughters, which in turn translates into poor friendships. I could not imagine being lonely and going through tough times without my true friends. Any person who has to go through life's challenges alone will find it difficult to overcome.

I don't know what I would do without my sister circle. They keep me sane. Sororities are a great way to create sisterhood bonds. I pledged AKA in college and that experience has provided me with lifelong girlfriends. We all share in a healthy reciprocal relationship with boundaries. My circle consists of about 15 women. We are all very close and many of us talk every day. My sister circle are a group of supportive, non-judgmental women who have my back. They tell me when I'm going in the wrong direction and help steer me back to safety. I think what I love most about my girlfriends is that they are all amazing women at the top of their game in many ways. Each one is successful in her personal and professional life.

The great thing is that I have another sister circle of women in my neighborhood. These women offer another view of life that is not catastrophic or unmanageable. They are comfortable in their own skin. They readily support each other and took me in without hesitation. One thing I have taken from their relationship is that I have to stop trying to rescue people who aren't calling out for help. I cannot emphasize this point enough: Every woman needs a good sister circle. It is important for our sanity and survival. As black women we have learned not to trust each other. We need one another and this is one negative cycle that we can break together. Let's start the conversation to help each other heal from our unresolved emotional trauma that leads to unhealthy behaviors and strained relationships. Emotions like anger, codependency, fear, jealousy and regret, create stress and anxiety in our mind and body. They hinder us from experiencing more positive emotions and enjoying life.

Anger

Women have a knack for tearing each other down. We've all encountered "mean girls" and bullies from elementary school through college and in our workplaces. Why are women so mean-spirited toward each other? More often than not, mean girls were raised by mean-spirited mothers who had strained relationships with other women—fear of competition, pettiness, jealousy, judgmental, and unsupportive. Mean, angry girls can grow up to be mean, angry women. Like stress, anger is a common emotion that we all experience when we are in survival mode of "fight" or "flight," that causes serious damage to our body. It's not healthy to be angry and mean all the time.

Unfortunately, many women carry anger with them for years which spills over into *all* of their relationships—at home with their children and partner, at work, at the store and even at church. Yes, there are a lot of mean, angry women in the church serving in leadership roles. Don't take it personal when your sisters who are routinely angry lash out at you. Their anger is likely a" cover-up" or mask to hide their insecurity and vulnerability.

Chances are they are in a bad cycle of anger-provoking moments called rumination and the slightest thing sets them off. Rumination sets in when you've experienced a negative emotion interacting with someone and you replay the incident over and over in your mind hundreds of different ways to the point that you are angry with anything or anyone in your path.

We should all pay careful attention to the frequency and severity of our anger to pinpoint our triggers. Television and other media make light of anger management classes and portray characters with severe anger issues for comedic effect. Being angry often to the point of rage is no joke. We need to intentionally practice ways to reduce our anger-triggers. Many of the steps to stress relief are similar to anger: practice breathing exercises, go for a walk, listen to calming music, progressive muscle relaxation, write in your journal or talk to a trusted friend. Misdirected anger does not have to ruin your relationships. Instead of tearing each other down, women need to build each other up. Offer up kind and encouraging words and tell your sister how wonderful and amazing she is today.

Codependency

One of the best examples of codependent relationships is depicted in the TV One series, *For My Man*. The show presents the tragic plight of women who will do *anything* for their man. I've been a guest on this show for a few episodes and codependency is the common thread connecting all of the women serving lengthy jail time. Codependency is an emotional disorder that arises when you totally ignore your own needs to your detriment. You become so emotionally attached to someone that you have known for a long time or even someone you recently met to fulfill their needs. As I mentioned, this behavior is evident in the actual stories on *For My Man* but it is also common in mother-daughter relationships and other family or close relationships in general.

More often than not, codependents have experienced some form of relationship trauma of their own so they gravitate toward unhealthy and unbalanced relationships due to low self-esteem. Codependents find themselves involved with people who are irresponsible, emotionally detached, or needy. They spend every ounce of their time and energy trying to save someone from themselves. Unfortunately, codependents are usually are left holding the bag for the other person because the other person does not want to be saved. This puts the codependents on an emotional rollercoaster causing severe distress and can lead to anxiety. It is a tragic cycle that I encounter often of women looking to men to fulfill their needs only to be left alone in one broken relationship to the next with children.

Common symptoms related to codependency include:

- Low self-esteem
- Self-denial
- Failure to set boundaries
- Control issues; perfectionism

For codependents suffering in silence, coping mechanisms tend to be alcohol abuse, drugs, sex or food. Therapy can help reduce the need for codependency and work on building healthy relationships.

Fear and Jealousy

Most fears in interpersonal relationships with women involve insecurity and jealousy. When you lack confidence and are insecure of your personal qualities or credentials you may lash out at other women because you fear not being good enough, fear being alone, fear rejection, fear failure or fear the competition. If this is you, listen up: you are more than enough. Make better choices in friendships. Surround yourself with supportive and empowering people. Even if you fail, its OK because failure is the best teacher that leads to success. Don't give up on your dreams and goals. Now if you're the woman who finds herself in that awkward, uncomfortable moment when your sister turns her back on you all of a sudden, more than likely she feels threatened by you because: i) You're intelligent, ii) You're happy; iii) You're in a thriving career; or iv) You're financially stable.

Instead of seeing these characteristics as resentful, you can flip the script and learn from your sister. Make time to get together just the two of you so you can let your guard down and be vulnerable. Ask questions about how she got started in her career, what steps she took to be stress-free, and what you can do to better manage your money. Black women can no longer afford to continue the vicious cycle of fear and jealousy amongst each other. We have to do better. Guys use the term "man up" which means to get tough and handle your business. Women need to start using the term "sister up" to encourage each other to lift each other up, handle our business and let go of the pettiness. Lives are at stake—our daughters and nieces are watching.

MINDFULNESS MOMENT

Logical mind (also known as reasonable mind) is just like it sounds. A person uses their logical mind when they consider only the facts. Logical mind is the "brain" of responses. Many people assume that logical mind is the "good" one; however, using only logic in many situations can be problematic. Think "cold" or "emotionless" when referring to the logical mind.

Emotional Mind is the attention-seeker of the three states of mind. A person uses their emotional mind when only feelings control thoughts and behavior. They may act impulsively and think about the consequences later. Think "hot headed" when referring to emotional mind.

Wise Mind is the balance of the two. Wise mind considers both logic and emotion to control thoughts and behaviors. A person uses their wise mind when they use the word "and" instead of "but" in decision-making. Balance is the key.

Challenge: Try to use "and" instead of "but" when problem-solving or communicating. For example, instead of "I love you but you make me angry" try saying "I love you and you make me angry at times". Use "and" in a variety of problem-solving situations.

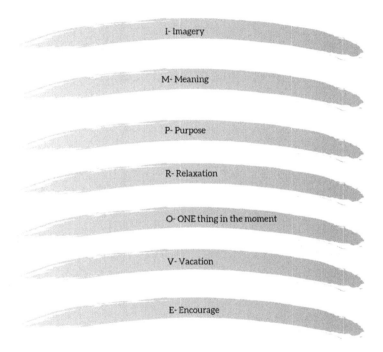

I- Imagery

M- Meaning

P- Purpose

R- Relaxation

O- ONE thing in the moment

V- Vacation

E- Encourage

PART II

LIES

"For there is nothing covered that will not be revealed, nor hidden that will not be known."
— **Luke 12:2 (NKJV)**

"Come to me, all you who are weary and burdened, and I will give you rest."
— Matt. 11:28 (NIV)

CHAPTER 6

Say Amen

As a Christian woman, I love God with all my heart. Yet as a doctor I believe the Christian culture is not helping those struggling with mental illness. Too many Christian leaders and others take on this self-righteous attitude when a person confides in them about negative thoughts and behaviors, by stating, "Just give it to God! Pray it away!" This mentality damages our community and leaves people confused and in the dark.

In church environments many people use the Bible as a silencer to cover up serious family abuses and other dysfunctions. For example, they say things like, "Don't speak things into existence, you are giving the devil too much information!" I have clients who were sexually abused by someone in their families. In most cases, they told their mothers and were not believed. For years these women have lived with their pain and suffered in silence. My thoughts have always been, *the Jesus that I know, would not want you to be pain and suffering.*" So many young girls leave the church hurt, embarrassed, and filled with shame. Unfortunately, they never return and young girls become women saddled with emotional baggage and trauma.

I remember another client who was a sexual trauma victim and was still dealing with a lot of emotional trauma. She also tried to speak out to the appropriate church leader and was told "don't say anything, there's nothing wrong with you!" As I processed this, the comment struck a nerve because as Christians we can be the biggest hypocrites in situations like this by failing to use intellect. Every thought is based on emotion and at the same time we deny those emotions that makes us uncomfortable. We witness spiritual leaders who are depressed and suicidal, yet the same leader encourages people about the importance of taking care of themselves. On the one hand, it's as if they are not flawed in this human cycle, but of course that's not true, so the mixed messages are confusing and many people are lost trying to deal with unresolved emotional trauma.

"If you teach people to think, they will find God."

— Dr. Caroline Leaf

In 2018, I watched a video of Dr. Caroline Leaf, a Cognitive Neuroscientist in a discussion with Pastor Steven Furtick of Elevation Church in North Carolina.[8] Dr. Leaf has studied the brain extensively for over two decades. She spoke about the cognitive dissonance between what we say when we quote Scripture as a culture and what we actually believe and do. We cannot speak Christian-ease all day and say "My God shall supply all my needs according to his riches in glory," and then constantly worry if we can pay our bills.

Dr. Leaf believes that religion has turned us into victims and we play the blame game. We give the devil a great deal of credit and we take no responsibility for our actions. She stressed, we can control our every thought. We have the power to do so. It's illogical that we intentionally damage our brain when we speak one way but our actions and later words say the opposite. For every sermon where we dance and shout about breakthroughs and breaking down strongholds, we fall into the same pattern before we get home. Our words and actions are toxic Christian-ease.

A Lifeway study indicated that nearly half of Evangelical Christians believe that mental illness can be overcome by Bible study and prayer alone.[9] The leader of the study believed that most Christians view mental illness as a character flaw and not a true illness. We need both doctors and our Christian faith. There were doctors in the Bible, yet Luke is the name most remembered as "the beloved physician" during his travels with the Apostle Paul.[10] The future is hopeful and clinicians and religious leaders need to come together to compliment each other. There are so many places in Scripture that line up with psychology, especially in the areas of mindfulness and Cognitive Behavioral Therapy (CBT), a form of psychotherapy that treats your problems by changing your behavior and seeks solutions to boost your happiness and thoughts. Great examples of depression can be seen in 1 Kings with the Prophet Elijah and several others.[11] God used people in the natural to do the work and seek wise counsel.

Part of the problem is that there is a lack of transparency between religious leaders. Again, some leaders think mental illness is a character flaw, while others believe that it is caused by unrepetence, lack of faith, demons or sin. On the opposite end of the spectrum are Christian leaders who remain silent as if mental illness does not exist which leaves people suffering and feel invisible in the church. These Believers with unmet needs disappear which is another missed opportunity for the church to fill an empty vessel.

God's Love

In God's eyes we are His daughters and He loves us unconditionally. Even during those moments when we feel unloved or missed the mark trying to accomplish something that we have been struggling to overcome—He still loves us and His love never fails. God knows everything about us; the good, the bad and the ugly. He gives us strength to overcome our weaknesses and the pure grace to cover the things that we are ashamed of. Therefore, always know that no matter where you are in your personal stress cycle or other mental health needs, hold fast to your faith in God. I encourage you to not give up on God because He won't give up on you!

"God, grant me the serenity to stop beating myself up for not doing things perfectly,

the courage to forgive myself because I'm working on doing things

better, and the wisdom to know that You already love me — just the way I am."

— Eleanor Brownn, The "Other" Serenity Prayer

"No one wants to expose the mental illness in the family, or the sexual abuser in the family because that person is at the dinner table on Thanksgiving."
— **Dr. RJ**

CHAPTER 7

Run And Tell That

S omewhere along the way women became sacrificial lambs. We sacrifice ourselves and our sanity to protect the predatory secrets of family members. This leads to daily slow deaths. We eat to make ourselves unattractive and invisible. We have convinced ourselves that if we continue to feed our emotions, our perpetrators will eventually be disgusted enough to leave us alone. We are internally silenced. Externally, we are told to be silent.

Where did this code of secrecy come from? Terrible things are happening to young women and the family, which is supposed to be our protector, turns their back and remains silent. Several studies show there is a link to the traumatic experiences of slavery to the relationships in the black community. The most prominent one was conducted by Dr. Joy DeGruy (Dr. Joy) on post-traumatic slave syndrome.[12] Dr. Joy's theory sheds light on the adaptive survival behaviors of Blacks in the U.S. and the diaspora as a result of multigenerational oppression from our African descendants. The slave mentally that Blacks were genetically inferior to whites continues as well as institutionalized racism all still affect Blacks today.

Dr. Joy found that because of the trauma and oppression,

"predictable patterns of behavior that tend to occur: i) **Vacant Esteem:**Insufficient development of primary esteem, along with feelings of hopelessness, depression and a general self destructive outlook; ii) **Marked Propensity for Anger and Violence**: Extreme feelings of suspicion perceived negative motivations of others. Violence against self, property and others, including the members of one's own group, i.e. friends, relatives, or acquaintances; and iii) **Racist Socialization and (internalized racism):** Learned Helplessness, literacy deprivation, distorted self-concept, and antipathy..."[13]

Dr. Joy's findings are remarkable and valid. The family unit in slavery consisted of a mother and child. Father-figures were rarely recognized. Men were devalued. Even if the father was considered, marriages were not legally recognized, so families were torn apart, and women were sexually abused. Throughout slavery, blacks had to suppress justifiable feelings of anger and outrage. Blacks had to suck it up and keep working, which was the pattern for hundreds of years and no one appears to be working to break that pattern overtly or covertly.

In addition, a similar pattern appears as a direct consequence; being a single, black, independent woman is cool. Black women have a history of not feeling protected by the head of family, for reasons out of everyone's control. These emotions are so strong and carry on from generation-to-generation and we don't even know why they still show up so strong. Black women need to speak up to change this disconnect as we are clear examples as to why this happens if no one speaks to it, then the cycle keeps on going.

Other casualties of "suck it up and keep working" lead to women feeling empowered to speak up and when we expressed ourselves we were labeled angry black women and seen in a negative light. This backlash only reinforced the notion that our thoughts and feelings don't matter. We tell ourselves, "Why say it? No one understands me, so how will talking about my problems help anyway?" All of this really stems from the history of slavery. In other (Western) cultures, women don't experience such a silencing and disregard. Black women have been automatically wired this way and we must be taught otherwise.

Another important silencer is secrecy and stigma. There were numerous secrets stemming from slavery. Shame, guilt, and regret, were prevalent as everything was about hiding something, yet it was not just for the sake of secrecy, it was for survival. Even in the Jim Crow Era it was important for survival then and today we have different tools. Although we use more advanced coping skills, secrecy within the family unit is still the elephant in the room. No one wants to expose the mental illness in the family, or the sexual abuser in the family because that person is at the dinner table on Thanksgiving. We all have a crazy uncle in the room that no one wants to talk about.

One final point on the effects of slavery in the family unit, is that historically, women of color have been stripped of our identity when we had to care for other people's children, while our children were at home. Back then, it was necessary for survival. Today, it's not necessary and doesn't make sense. The result of mom not being in the home created a situation where little girls were placed in caretaking roles as early as age seven and started taking care of other children on the plantation. We have been part of a tradition where losing innocence at an early age was normal.

Changing the Narrative

Black boys also have a history of being viewed as a threat when they are actually children. According to a psychological study in 2014 to determine implicit racial bias, participants were shown photos of a five-year-old Black boy. When participants were asked how they felt about the child, their emotional response was "fear." [14] In another study, white university students were shown photos of Black boys under nine years old, they believed he was more culpable in committing a violent crime than a white or Latino male. [15] Study results and the current racial climate in America add credence to the fact that childhood innocence of Black boys and girls is disregarded in society.

Impartial racial bias against Black children is alive in well. "Girl Interrupted" was a 2017 study by Georgetown University Law Center on Poverty and Equality found that Black girls as young as five years old were viewed by adults as "less innocent and more adult-like than white girls of the same age."[16] As part of the study they created a childhood innocence scale which included other stereotypes about Black girls and women. Even more disturbing is that the adults surveyed saw Black girls as needing less protection than white girls, and viewed Black as more independent, knowledgeable about sex, and need less nurturing and support than white children.[17]

Our children need us to do better. As many of you can attest, our parents disciplined us severely. Research showed that "Black children are disciplined more frequently and harshly than their white peers, and are almost four times as likely as their white counterparts to be suspended from school."[18] Not only do we have to talk to our sons and daughters about these racial biases, we have to encourage them not to buy into the negative perceptions and put forth their best efforts at all times. We can't expect anyone to change the narrative on our behalf— it's up to us.

"We dance round in a ring and suppose, but the secret sits in the middle and knows."
— Robert Frost, *The Secret Sits*

CHAPTER 8

Pandora's Box

My grandmother died in September 2018 of depression and Alzeheimer's disease. Her death was a few days after Hurricane Florence. At the time, to my knowledge I was the only grandchild on my father "Jesse's" side. My grandfather passed away three years prior. I was very close to my grandparents throughout my life and lived with them at times. Now losing both of them was devastating. Due to the storm, my flight to Hampton, Virginia was cancelled. I was stressed about not being there for the funeral. I was determined to pay my respects and drove to Virginia. Thankfully, I was part of her homegoing celebration.

Days leading up to the funeral, I felt a sensation in the pit of my stomach that something wasn't right with my relationship with my father "Jesse." I began having doubt as to whether he was really my father. He approached me at the funeral and said, "Well if I am not your father, will you still let me see my grandkids?" *Really? How can you ask me this now? I wouldn't do that to my kids.*

Even though I am an adult and my children and husband are connected to my father, the next month I asked "Jesse," the man I had known as my dad since birth, to do an ancestry DNA test to be sure. The results came back showing that there was no match! Nothing in our DNA was even close. At over 40 years old, I found out that Jesse was not my father. My grandparents whom I loved and they loved me more, were of no blood relation to me. To say I was devastated is an understatement. This is the type of news you see in a movie or dramatic television series. *I can't believe this is happening in my life. Now? At my age!*

I began questioning other family and friends. A few months later, another man surfaced. His name was Walter and he is the younger brother of my mom's best friend. For years, Walter told others that I was his daughter. I found out that he wanted me to be in his wedding when I was 16 years old because there was no doubt that I was his daughter. That summer, my mother sent me to visit with him to get to know him—talk about confusing! I thought it was strange when he wanted me to keep in touch with him even though I took a liking to him. I finally contacted him after all these years and told him about "Jesse" and the DNA test results.

"I am your father and I have tried to be in your life forever. Your mother said you were too close to your grandparents and it would be too disruptive, so I didn't push the issue but I should have."

"This is so crazy. I need closure. I cannot keep going on like this. I would really like for you to do the DNA test."

"Absolutely. Whatever you need."

Although Walter and I had a few things in common, I decided I wanted to wait until I was 100% sure as I did not want to expose my kids to another "grandpa" after revealing the truth about Jesse. A few months later, the results were in. Drumroll please...Walter and I are a zero match! I couldn't believe my eyes. I was devastated. Walter's spirit was crushed and he did not believe it. Now he wanted to do an actual paternity test. I told him that the results were accurate. I thought it would be best to wait a few days after the Christmas holiday to avoid the unnecessary stress. I felt bad for Walter who spent 39 years thinking I was his daughter. He was such a nice, respectable man. I wasn't quite sure how to process this all out so I leaned on my sister circle. All I wanted was answers. I wasn't OK, and to add insult to injury, my mom had no answers.

Daddy's Little Girl

"What makes you a man is not the ability to
have a child — it's the courage to raise one."

— President Barack Obama

Of course no one is perfect but as a child you want your parents to be the best human beings you ever met. Growing up with an inconsistent father-figure created emotional insecurities as a child that I could not articulate. Many times I questioned if he loved me or cared anything about me. I held on to the traditional role of a father; to protect his little girl until she was ready for marriage. I wanted to be "daddy's little girl" but instead I wore the badge of "daddy issues" without realizing it until therapy.

I can't help but reflect on all those years where I longed for my dad's attention. I had deep daddy issues. As a child, it taught me that men were incompetent, undependable and emotionally unavailable. I felt this way even though I had two prominent men in my life, my uncle and grandfather but the actual father was an essential missing piece.

My heart was so torn for many years. Other women may have seen me in my 20's as very arrogant, dismissive and cold in relationships. None of that changed until I went to therapy. This all came out in therapy in graduate school with my first therapist, a Jewish man in Long Island. He told me that I could not relax because my soul was not rested. He said I was emotionally empty. *You talkin' to me? Who you calling emotionally empty?* I am grateful to this doctor because he humbled me and the healing began. After that year I wanted more and I continued to go. If I had not gone to therapy I would have been a jacked-up person today and missed out on a lot of good people in my life. Women need to know that they are not alone. This does not discriminate. The absent father issue impacts us all in a way that we cannot process alone.

As a therapist, I've learned that whether you have a great dad, terrible dad, absent dad or indifferent dad, fathers have a great influence in our lives. It bothered me that no matter how successful I was in my career or happy in my marriage, and even fulfilled by my sister circle, I still wanted my father's approval. I yearned for this loving relationship from someone who did not deserve it. I longed for validation and words of encouragement but they never came. Validating words from a girl's father are essential to her growth and development. Regardless of how old you are, bringing closure to your tenuous or strained relationship with your father will help improve your relationships with men and women in the long run. In my case, God had a mind-blowing, healing plan.

"I cannot think of any need in childhood as strong as the need for a father's protection."
— **Sigmund Freud**

CHAPTER 9

Maury Moment

I n early 2019 a man named Bobby popped up in my immediate family squares on Ancestry.com. He got my information and called my job. I called him back and it turned out that he was my uncle. We talked for a few moments and then just like that, we figured out who my biological father was. He had one brother who lived in Hampton, Virginia. He ended the call and said he would have his brother call me back.

We took an official DNA test and it came back 99.9% that Bobby's brother was my father! Initially, my mother did not remember him nor did he remember her. My father's name is "Carl." He is from North Carolina but lived in Hampton my whole life. He does not have daughters and has a son four years older than me, and another son with his wife.

So thanks to my uncle Bobby, I have connected with my father and new family. I talk to Carl often and he visited my family this past Easter. He is a really nice man and his wife was excited to meet me because he did not have a daughter. Before we took the DNA test she saw my photo and said, "Oh that is definitely your father." It continues to be a very spiritual moment. Our relationship is comfortable and genuine. My mom gave me a heartfelt apology for the first time in my life. She is relieved that I found him and knows how important this was to me. I accepted her apology and we are on better terms.

New Beginnings

I was talking to my best friend at dinner about the importance of knowing who you are and where you come from. I realized that there was a void in that part of my life. My grandparents were wonderful. I am glad that they were not alive to learn that I was not their blood grandchild. The bond, love, and connection we shared goes beyond any title. Now, when I am talking to my dad Carl and he says, "Oh sweetheart, how was your day?" I smile on the inside. I was not expecting this impact at 40 years old. In my mind, my "daddy issues" were resolved. I guess in my heart they weren't. When Carl speaks to me, I don't feel like this grown woman that I am projecting. Instead, I feel like a little girl who has found her daddy.

Each day is really a new beginning. When we talk on the phone our timing is perfect and we have a natural flow. Carl is warm and his voice is comforting. He is gentle but firm and does not seem passive but warm and approachable. We are finding out our similarities like Carl and I both drink green smoothies every day. My dad is not much of a talker, unless he has something to say. He is smart, handsome, stylish, and has a strong work ethic. He is also an ordained minister but not overly religious. Spirituality is a part of who he is and I know I have that piece from him.

I feel like I would have been a better wife if Carl had been in my life from the beginning. I would definitely have been a better communicator. I was 27 when I got married and emotionally immature. I had a disregard for other people's feelings. My actions were a reflection of learned behavior in my home. It was the only way I knew how to act, even though it never felt right.

How has this impacted my family? Well, it was hard for my husband because he was really close to my grandparents. He was more hurt about that. I explained to him that your family is not necessarily blood. He was worried about me at first, and now he is excited that I finally have closure. When we decided to talk to our kids about everything, I explained how when people get married they gain a family member and I now gained a new family member. My son Ryan is excited about more people and more grandpas to play with. Ryan says Carl and I have the same eyes which fills me with joy. Carl, and my paternal side of the family have brought so much peace, happiness, pride, and closure to my life. For once, I am truly a "daddy's girl."

Puzzle Pieces

We talk a lot about mothers, not fathers. From a general psychological standpoint, your sense of self is fragmented. Once those pieces come together and it is integrated it becomes a pushing and pulling until learned behaviors are molded. Reintegration puts the puzzle together like it is supposed to be. This is a reintegration period for me. For other women who have an opportunity to be reintegrated, definitely accept it and take the feelings moment by moment. If you are going through any type of reintegration I recommend therapy. Like all of us, we need to process anger, sadness, feelings of abandonment, regret, and the countless what if's.

Be mindful that there will be a cycle of grief that will resurface. Being able to reintegrate yourself and making a "new" normal by knowing who you are will automatically heal emotional voids. I am still getting used to these intense feelings, allowing myself to feel, instead of pushing my feelings aside. The process is not as clear. This reintegration of self and being in the moment has competing forces: who do I let in and who do I keep out along this journey with me? These thoughts bring up feelings of vulnerability and I have invested so much time filling in these emotional holes with bandaids and silly putty and they are finally all wearing off. This stage of vulnerability is unnerving but you have to go for it, approach it, be brave, and take it day-by-day, moment-by-moment. You will see that the outcome of a fully integrated self is totally worth it.

"You realize, don't you, that you are the temple of God, and God himself is present in you? No one will get by with vandalizing God's temple, you can be sure of that. God's temple is sacred—and you, remember, are the temple."
—1 Corinthians 3:17-20 (MSG)

CHAPTER 10

A Living Temple

Women of color are the most beautiful, unique human beings on the planet. With our range of skin tones, facial features, hair, and body shapes, it's no wonder that women of other cultures desire to capture our essence—fuller lips, hips, and buttocks. When we step out of the house, we have to put up with catcalls, gawks, and embarrassingly rude behavior from men. The anatomy of Black women has been objectified for centuries. One of the most tragic stories of objection can be seen in the life and death of Sara Baartman.

For those who do not know Sara's story, there are several documentaries and articles about her "freak show" existence that are worth reading.[19] Sara was born in a rural cattle-herding village in Khoisan, in the Eastern Cape of Africa. Her parents died by the time she reached adolescence and in the early 1800s, Sara was sold into slavery and then purchased by a European doctor when she was 16 years old. She became a freak show throughout the United Kingdom and Paris because of the large fatty tissue in her thighs and buttocks, and was named "Hottentot Venus." She was considered a primitive phenomenon of nature and her half-naked body was on display for men to gawk at for a small fee. If they wanted to touch her they paid a little more. These men were both curious about Black women, and also had sexually pervasive fantasies about us, despite believing that indigenous African women were abnormal and inferior.

After her years on display in London, she was sold to an animal handler in France where she was caged like an animal, responding to commands from a "trainer," all while her female organs were on display. Despite the fact that Sara was multilingual and spoke her native language as well as French, Dutch, and English, she was considered inferior to that of an orangutan. She died in 1815 at the age of 26 from what was believed to be an inflammatory disease related to syphilis, smallpox, alcoholism, and pneumonia.

Not only was Sara's short life a tragedy, but her death proved to be more tragic. Her body was taken by French naturalist, George Cuvier who made a plaster cast of her body before dissecting it. Cuvier then pickled her brain and genitalia and put them in jars on display at the *Musée de l'Homme* in Paris. Cuvier believed that he proved his theory of racial evolution—Blacks are sexually primitive with the intelligence equal to orangutans. It's truly hard to imagine that Sara's remains were in that museum from 1815 until 1974. It wasn't until Nelson Mandela became the President of South Africa that he went to great lengths to have Sara's remains returned to her home country. She was buried in a small village near her hometown on August 9, 2002, over 200 years later. Sara's story hurts on so many levels, especially when I think about the perception of young black girls today.

When They See "You"

It's been over 200 years since Sara Baartman's death and I'm afraid that not much has changed. The stereotypes and negative perceptions are exacerbated now more than ever due to social media and instant access to information. We have gotten to the point where there is no limit to what we will do in front of a camera or video recorder for attention. Women are risking their lives for butt injections by non-doctors, for the sake of beauty and attention. Those who survive these botched cosmetic procedures end up with health issues and permanent damage.

Let's face it, there are social and cultural influences in the Black community that may not be advantageous for us in the long run, specifically in the areas of music and fashion. Music has a huge influence on our emotional state and the barrage of hip-hop lyrics labeling women in degrading terms has become the norm. I don't think people realize the effect these negative terms and attention-seeking behaviors have on emotions and self-esteem.

Not only has the music become ingrained in our culture, Black influence on fashion is undeniable. Our unique style and creativity to "slay" on a budget turns heads wherever we go. We do our best to model celebrity fashion icons yet oftentimes, the risque fashion choices of celebrities as a whole, are not conducive to strut on the runway of our everyday lives. Sexy lingerie and undergarments have become a fashion norm for young women today. Of course it's great to look and feel sexy but we must have limits. In a broader sense it doesn't help our challenge as women of color to change the narrative and erase the negative stereotypes about our sexual prowess, need for attention, and willingness to be down for anything. These types of lies has fueled the perception by men that Black women don't deserve to be respected. More than ever we must be respected as wives, mothers, sisters, daughters, aunts and girlfriends. Trust me, we can still be beautiful and unbelievably sexy without baring it all.

Health Check

In general, there are certain diseases that affect Black women disproportionately than whites and other races. We have higher incidences of mortality rates after being diagnosed with heart disease, stroke, diabetes, and breast and cervical cancer. In addition, Black women report mental illness symptoms more than whites. The stigma of being associated with mental illness in the Black community has caused many to suffer in silence and never seek treatment. First things first—we have to take care of our mind to help create a healthy pathway to take care of our bodies.

A 2016 report from the American Heart Association found that 46 of every 100,000 black women died from strokes, whereas 35 of every 100,000 white women also died. The rates for diabetes diagnosis in Black women is higher than whites.[20] All of these high risk illnesses factors into your weight and eating habits. Finding a balance between good and bad fats, low cholesterol foods, and limiting sugar, fried and processed foods in exchange for fresh fruits and vegetables can change your outlook.

Another medical issue affecting Black women more than their counterparts is STDs. While rates of certain cases of STDs have decreased such as chlamydia and gonorrhea, we still outpace other ethnicities with the number of new diagnoses in syphilis, HIV, and AIDS. It's ironic how Blacks are perceived as knowledgeable and experienced in sexual activity, when sex and intimacy are not openly talked about in our homes and in the community, so conversations around protected sex are not happening as often as they should. Many STDs can be prevented and treatment options are available nationwide.

It's time to stop the dysfunctional cycle of lies and secrets impacting the Black community as it relates to our mind and body. A healthy mind creates a healthy body. We have to be vulnerable and let our guard down and ask for help. There's no time to wait or hold back information. Have open, honest conversations with your primary care physician when you feel something is not right emotionally or physically. Schedule your yearly exams, show up, ask questions, and follow your doctor's orders. We've all been given this one sacred temple and we must do everything we can to take care of it.

"Someone was hurt before you, wronged before you, hungry before you, frightened before you, beaten before you, humiliated before you, raped before you...yet, someone survived... You can do anything you choose to do."
– Dr. Maya Angelou

CHAPTER 11

Cover Girls: Everyday Artists

Our past is behind us but the effects of negative emotions and behaviors linger and hold us back from healthy experiences. We need to heal and stop hiding. Women can mask their pain, trauma, anxiety, insecurity, and other emotional wounds with makeup, hair, and a killer wardrobe. By day we are superwomen, by night we are emotional wrecks—angry, confused, exhausted, hurt, sad, and stressed. We suffer from insomnia because we cannot relax our mind long enough to get a decent night's rest. I'm blessed to be able to help my clients manage their emotions and mental health and lead productive lives. No matter how many clients I see, there are common themes amongst the women that each of us can relate to. None of the "Cover Girl" stories represent one or two clients but they are a combination of several clients over my years in practice. I thought it would be helpful to share a few of these experiences to help you move closer to making a decision to end your cycle of negative thought patterns of behavior.

Type 1 - Supermom

Background/Profile - Beautiful, smart, perfectionist. Picture-perfect family. She has a handsome husband who is successful. The kids are smart, gorgeous, and attend private school. The family takes several vacations each year across the globe. They are adored by anyone they come in contact with in public. Behind closed doors is a different story.

Supermom tries to give her children everything she did not have as a child and often the children are not well-behaved as they are ungrateful. She sees herself as a failure as a parent and wife. Her husband views her as cold and withholding affection but what she really fears is rejection and she doesn't like to be vulnerable. She comes across as bitter, mean, and is easily saddened and isolates herself at times.

When she came into therapy she blurted, "I'm just a total mess! My girlfriend told me that she has a therapist so I decided to just give it a try." Once we started, she talked a little bit more about how she cheated and wanted to leave her husband but could not do it to her kids. Then she found out that her husband cheated so now she wanted to divorce him yet he wants to salvage the marriage.

Supermom is a master at putting on appearances that everything is OK. Her sister has MS so she makes time to care for her and give her everything she needs. Her mother is a retired nurse and she was molested by a family member that no one ever talks about. Her father is a Vietnam Veteran and drug abuser so he was constantly unemployed because of his addiction. Growing up, her family did not have material things.

Her mother badgers her when she tries to talk to her and often responds with, "If it wasn't for me you wouldn't be anything!" Initially, when I asked about her family she said, "What? My sister and I had a perfect childhood." She then wanted to know why she needed to talk about her family and I explained that it will help if we can see patterns. "Apparently, I am the one who was destined to fail," she added. This is how she talks about herself over and over. After discussing more about her family I was able to show her patterns in her own behavior and how she could begin to change them.

She is also very explosive and obsessive with details and has her kids in a ton of activities. Supermom is the Energizer Bunny, always going, going, going and her husband feels left out and neglected. She does not let him help out because she thinks he would mess it up, especially since her father was physically present but emotionally absent. She has no frame of reference to see how a family could work together as a team. At the end of the day, Supermom is exhausted, has a low-self esteem, is overly stressed, and on medication for anxiety. But on the outside, she is picture perfect.

Therapy with supermom would begin with a genogram, exploring patterns, and increasing insight.

Type 2 - Traumatized

Background/Profile - This is a woman who has been a victim of sexual trauma and molestation by a family member as a child and never told anyone. Most female adults convince themselves, *why bring it out now, it happened so many years ago?* Then after seeking therapy, she realizes that some of her problems like weight gain (she eats to self-soothe and food is reliable) are because she is always on empty. Now she struggles with self-confidence because she does not like the way she looks and it creates sadness and isolation.

I've had several consultations with traumatized women between the ages of 40 and 52 who are in therapy but came to me for an evaluation because they felt they needed more. A few years ago I consulted with a 48-year-old Black woman who revealed a ton of unbelievable trauma, yet she goes to work every single day and somehow functions. Her Adverse Childhood Experiences (ACE) score was eight out of 10. This essentially means that everything bad that could have happened before she turned 18, did in fact happen. In her adult life, her boyfriend shot her in both arms in a jealous rage because he thought she was "hugging up" on another man. This incident left her with constant pain in both arms and hands for years. The following year she was jumped by several women who claimed her daughter bullied one of their daughters. The damage from that beating was still evident after 10 years. She has a lot of trauma, a lot of triggers, including her mother physically abusing her. This woman was also sexually abused and exposed to poverty. She does not self-medicate and reports constant thoughts of suicide. She stated that her only reason for living was for her children. There are so many women walking around with incomprehensible bad things that have happened to them. They are surviving but suffering. Research shows that high ACE experiences lead to substance abuse, obesity, alcoholism, and early death if there is no treatment. The emotional trauma lingers and there is a direct correlation to physical death. It is important to acknowledge that it impacted you so you can work even harder to get treatment.

I still think about these types of women and hope they remain in therapy and reveal their truthful life events. As Black people or people of color, we walk around with so much trauma that it becomes our norm, while for other cultures, self-care is the norm. Although there is inequity in the availability of resources for people of color, little by little we can close the gap if we acknowledge a problem, seek help, and take care of our mental health. Therapy will be long term initially using a trauma-focused approach and cognitive behavorial therapy.

Type 3 - Undiagnosed mental illness

Background/Profile - This woman is very active in church and may seem hyper religious yet she has a lot of depression and anxiety. She also has several secrets that she is not ready to reveal. Tragically, her secrets are so severe that she has attempted suicide and cuts her arms and legs. The pain is so bad but she endures it to substitute the emotional pain. She is easily agitated and always late. Her secrets keep her on edge and allows her to hide behind her super religious environment because in general, the church does not talk about mental illness. When she is faced with any stress, she falls apart and quits, but jumps back in because she is a worker; a busy worker-bee, and people want her around because she gets the job done.

In particular, this woman was having trouble sleeping because her mind is always racing. She wakes up wakes up in the middle of the night to go to the bathroom and freezes like a deer in headlights. She has flashbacks of when she was younger and her uncle would wake up and follow her to the bathroom to molest her. When she was a child, she wet the bed so that she did not have to deal with her uncle, and even now she avoids late night trips to the restroom.

Trauma-focused cognitive beharorial therapy would be beneficial for this woman.

Type 4 - Over achiever

Background/Profile - This beautiful woman has been in and out of a lot of relationships. She is very smart, single with no children, and has fertility challenges. She dates often and is an impeccable dresser. As an overachiever, she is involved in several professional and social activities. She is a world traveler and lives the lifestyle of a socialite. But behind it all, her self-worth is low and she feels if she died no one would notice. She believes that she is not needed in her environment.

This type of woman needs to be validated and feels that having a child may be her way of being noticed by people. It could be a learned behavior or an emotional response to rejection from the past. She distracts herself with monthly marathons, obsessive exercise, and nonstop social interaction. Her main question is do I matter? When I die will people miss me?

The first thing I seek to do is help her meet basic needs. Keeping her job is important. Then I use Cognitive Behavioral Therapy (CBT), which teaches the relationship between thoughts, feelings and behavior. Overall, this therapy is about building rapport. Listening. Providing a safe environment, then creating a corrective emotional experience by providing validation. It is important that she knows that she is valued and the goal is to rebuild herself. We create affirmations, rest, and ensure proper eating habits. Erasing negative self-talk and erasing it with true statements is the key.

Type 5 - Golden Child/Family Jewel

Background/Profile - Most of the time there is a sibling or parent that expects a lot of them. Living life for someone else and not themselves. Their life set up like a resume. When they check off all the boxes they still feel empty. This person has bought into the false narrative that we are supposed to be married with children, but they are so empty and incomplete because they are lacking in this area.

Stress and overachieving attributes to loneliness emptiness and unflattering messages continue to play in her head. Her thoughts are, "I am doing all this and it is not going to matter anyway." Whatever failures she's had are false evidence of her shortcomings. This overachiever also appears picture-perfect in public and people admire her from afar but she goes home lonely and depressed. She feels like her problems are not that significant because they are personal problems but she does not realize that they keep her from being whole.

She typically has a long day and wakes up at 4:30 AM to run a mile regardless of weather. She lives off protein shakes and is healthy and in shape. She is a fashionista with a double walk-in closet organized by season and color—even her shoes. She listens to classical music to destress as she drives around in a gold Maserati. She is the first in her family to own a home. She attended an HBCU and received her Masters from Harvard. When she arrives home at 11 PM her house is empty and quiet. She is not currently dating. Many guys are intimidated by her so she attracts flaky guys. Coming home after a long day highlights the loneliness of her empty home. She has passive suicidal thoughts as her last statement before bed is "Why am I here?"

By morning she plays her own tape recorder in her head and it is filled with negative thoughts. She feels hopeless, worthless, and can't seem to find her purpose or passion. The day starts all over again like the last and the only emotion she feels is lonely.

Psychoeducation about the impact of chronic stress on the brain and body is a good place to begin therapy with the over-achiever.

Type 6 - Absent mother

Background/Profile - When thinking about this type of women, the old adage comes to mind, "Don't throw the baby out with the bathwater." Sadly, this scenario happens often; an absent mother believes she is doing the right thing for her family but it has damaging effects.

Robin grew up in extreme poverty. She always felt like she was missing out on a huge part of life by not having the latest outfits, gadgets and even basic necessities. She got married at 22 to a man ten years her senior. He appeared stable and hard-working. Robin became pregnant right after the marriage and gave birth to twin girls. A year later she gave birth to their son. Being married with children never stopped her from pursuing her dream of becoming a lawyer. Throughout law school, her husband and friends have cared for her children. She worked non-stop in school and upon graduation, she got a job at one of the top firms in the country which meant she was on call nearly seven days a week working on a "big" case.

Since Robin was never home, she felt guilty and provided her kids with lavish gifts that she could not afford and paid for expensive vacations for them to enjoy with other relatives. Robin takes care of everyone in her family financially and loans large sums of money to family members whom she knows can never pay her back. To add to her stress and anxiety, her husband is a drug abuser and she is his enabler.

Her twin daughters are now 16 and her son is 15. All three children are dealing with some form of mental illness. One of her daughters is a drug abuser as she began getting high with her dad at 12 years old. The other daughter is in and out of abusive and codependent relationships. Her son has already survived a few suicide attempts. He feels totally neglected by his mom as she was never there. This young man suffers from deep depression.

Robin has been having panic attacks and was trying to handle her stressful situation her own. Fortunately, a close friend convinced her to seek professional help. Women like Robin think they are doing a good thing by providing materials things. All three children felt neglected and had no outlet to express their feelings. Their father also felt neglected and used drugs and alcohol as an escape.

A lot of times when I do Genograms with my clients, we look at patterns and initially, we think we are doing better than the previous generation when in reality we are actually doing more damage. We must learn to take things from our past that we were not happy with and discard them. As women, we tend to only think about the bad and we try to do the complete opposite and then we mess it up; it's extreme black and white thinking, so we miss the gray area. Balance is key.

Type 7 - Severe childhood trauma

Background/Profile: This strong, resilient woman of color has six children ranging in age from elementary school to adulthood. All six children have different fathers. She was repeatedly raped by her father as a child and gave birth to her first child by her father at 14 years old. Her mother was fully aware of the father's sexual abuse and did nothing. She ran away often but came back home as she had nowhere to go. She and her mother often came to blows over the pregnancy. Her mother refused to let her have an abortion or put the baby up for adoption.

Her childhood home was extremely dysfunctional as there were other siblings in the home that were also being molested but they were fortunate to be sent away to live with relatives. She was also molested by her oldest brother and uncle. All three of these abusive men are still part of her life and she sees them often—father, brother, and uncle. This cover girl is extremely traumatized. Her attachment to her children is also an issue because it is unhealthy. She totally smothers her children as she does not want them to go through anything like she did. Unfortunately, the downside is that her children have very poor social skills and cannot interact with others their age. They have extensive absences from school and are far behind in their grade level. Our sister's unresolved severe childhood trauma can have damaging effects for future generations if help is not provided to the entire family.

Therapy will be long-term. A top down approach will likely be the most effective where the therapist helps her to stabilize her current life prior to delving into the past by using a trauma-focused approach.

The Deadly Cost of Hidden Suffering

Oftentimes, women of trauma convince themselves that it was their fault because of what a perpetrator did to them. The self-talk lies about themselves that keeps them from seeking help or speaking out. What lies do you tell yourself daily?

- ◉ I am not good enough

- ◉ I am not smart enough

- ◉ I have no value

- ◉ I am not picture perfect ...

These types of cognitive distortions are a key factor in therapy. I ask my patients all the time, "When did you decide to build a fort around your heart? How old were you when you decided to protect yourself?" Now that they are adults, it is not necessary and there are things they can do to protect themselves yet they have built a fort that keeps everything out... good and bad.

Lies Debunked

"I got a lot to be mad about."

— Solange Knowles

Black women have been the subject of negative and hurtful press for years. Whether it is First Lady Michelle Obama being called an "angry black woman" or an ape, these types of misguided labels have penetrated mainstream society. Serena Williams, one of the top most powerful women in tennis for decades has been labeled an "angry black woman," not to mention the unflattering remarks hurled at her for her beautiful, strong, physique. Why such negative labels? Fear? Jealousy? Sometimes we tear each other down by repeating these stereotypes to each other. This is something that we can control. We have to respect, and treat our sisters like Queens and not to add fuel to an already negatively heightened environment. The list of lies can go on but for now it's up to us to nip them in the bud and correct those who continue along this path.

- Black women are angry;

- Black women have a bad attitude;

- Black women are aggressive;

- Black women emasculate men;

- Black girls are "fast tails;

- Black women are Loud, Unclassy, "Ghetto";

- Black Men don't love us when they reach a certain status;

- Black women are promiscuous...sexuality is bad; Sex is for men

- Black women were lied to by their mothers: "good girls don't do it," "kiss a boy and you could get pregnant.

- Black women contradict womanhood: "Be about your books, leave them boys alone," "Get a good job, pay your own bills, don't be depending on no man, keep a 'go to hell fund', but then at some random magic age the message becomes different and "independent woman" is a negative phrase and derogatory;

- Black women's tears are a sign of weakness; and

- Black women are only good for child-bearing/nurturing—if they do anything else it makes them 'hard' or 'aloof.'

Do we have a right to be upset at times? Yes! Let's be real, the truth of the matter is that Black women have carried the burdens of everyone on their shoulders throughout history (Yoruba tribes in Africa, transatlantic slave trade, colonization/slavery). We have supported our Black men throughout the Civil Rights Movement, Vietnam, the 80's crack cocaine epidemic and the disproportionate mass incarceration. STOP telling us to smile. We have a right to be angry about social injustice, oppression, and abuse. Look at how our anger has changed nations and the course of history: Harriett Tubman, Sojourner Truth, Maxine Waters, Serena Williams, and countless other strong, Black women.

Our young girls continue to be exploited with cat calls, verbal abuse, and hit records degrading us at every turn. Many of our girls are made to be ashamed of their developing bodies which feeds into the rape culture and victim blaming. We've already seen the tragic story of Sara Baartman's objectification and exploitation, and then years later during Reconstruction women were bound by the Bible and modesty or being "lady-like" was demanded—anything less, you were labeled by your community as a "hoe", "slut," or today's term, "thot." We have to change how we speak to each other or the lies will continue to flourish. Again, it's all part of changing the narrative. More than anything, we must continue to be loud—loud enough to win elections, change nations, and save lives. Black girl magic is real.

PART III

VACANCY

"You abandoned me, Love don't live here anymore.
Just a vacancy, love don't live here anymore."
— **Rolls Royce**

*"A person's readiness to date is largely
a matter of maturity and
environment."*
—Dr. Myles Munroe

CHAPTER 12

Dating

For most of us, dating can be one of the most stressful aspects of our lives. It's a time where we go through extreme emotional highs and lows. This is on top of the emotionally depleting relationships at work or at home. Whether you are dating in a more traditional method or online, the dating process can be complicated so knowing what to expect can help you navigate your path. Wouldn't it be great if we all found our perfect match sharing a common bond like Sanaa Latham and Omar Epps in *Love & Basketball*? Or if we experienced an instant connection like Nia Long and Larenz Tate in *Love Jones*? Unfortunately, our lives don't play out like the happy endings of our favorite romantic movies and we are left with the negative effects that dating has on our psychological and emotional well-being. As with all interpersonal relationships, we go through stages or phases of contentment, excitement, disappointment, and even devastation. For our purposes I'd like to touch upon three dating stages: i) Attraction; ii) Exclusivity, and iii) Intimacy.

Butterflies

I like to think of the attraction phase as the "butterflies in your stomach" stage. It's when you are bursting at the seams at the mere thought of your love interest. This is where you find out that you have several things in common and there is a strong emotional and physical chemistry — you're together often and can't keep your hands off each other. It's also the conflict avoidance stage and you will do anything to avoid conflict. Yes, it definitely feels amazing. In reality, your brain is releasing oxytocin, a hormone that has been called the "cuddle hormone" or "love hormone" which initiates your desire to bond or snuggle with someone. Oxytocin also plays a major role in childbirth and mother and baby bonding. This hormone's strong release makes us feel like we're in "love" and we immediately attach positive feelings and emotions towards our love interest, even if we see red flags. Oxytocin also invokes feelings of trust, stability, and warm and fuzzy. For example, a woman's dating trajectory may look like the following:

i) physical attraction,

ii) desire to be with the person,

iii) start a relationship,

iv) bond, and

v) start to build.

Men on the other hand are guided by testerone and their dating trajectory might look like:

i) physical attraction;

ii) desire to be with you;

iii) start a relationship;

iv) bond,

v) sex, and

vi) repeat the challenge (which increases his testerone).

As you can see, men and women are guided by different hormones. Both men and women have testosterone yet women have much less. Men release testosterone at higher levels in the beginning of dating but as the relationship lingers, their levels go down which makes them prone to serial dating and being noncommittal. Research shows that testosterone levels decrease in both men and women in committed relationships versus singles. Developing a relationship requires time, attention, and patience. Take it slow in order to get to know each other emotionally and physically. In time, you both will be comfortable and on the same page to make decisions about whether or not to move to the next stage. My grandmother used to say, "You need to know a man for all seasons first." I believe in essence she was saying don't let your hormones make the final decision.

We Go Together

If you're still going strong for a few months you start to enter into the reality stages of exclusivity, also known as "settling." In order to avoid any misunderstandings, make sure you both have a conversation about not seeing other people and being committed to each other. Many times when things are going pretty well, one person assumes that the relationship is exclusive and the other person is not fully on board. Be sure you are both clear. By now, you are both in a comfort zone. You start to see flaws in each other that are annoying, although they were always present but you didn't want to rock the boat. The chemistry is still there, but not as hot and heavy as in the beginning. You both have settled into the routine of a committed relationship and wonder where things are headed.

Chances are you and your partner are talking more honestly and open at this time. Arguments are likely to creep in as emotional wounds are opened up from previous relationships. For example, your love interest pours on constant criticism, becomes moody or angry if your late or things don't go as planned, or just plain and simple, every little thing becomes an issue. Negative patterns become more clear and you both are trying to find ways to appease each other but its superficial—you're unhappy and angry on the inside but you still feel a tug in your heart for this person. You keep asking yourself, *Why can't it be like it was before?* Medically speaking, your body can't keep up that elated feeling forever so your emotional high dissipates. Hang in there. Your relationship is not doomed. Don't get too comfortable and stop doing the things that made the other person feel special. Try to maintain strong communication and let the walls down. If there is trust and a commitment to work together as a team, you will likely move past this stage.

Is This the One?

The intimacy stage is where you are determining if the relationship will last for the long haul. Is this person committed to a life-long journey with me? Am I committed to a lifelong journey with him? During this time, you should have connected with your love interest on all four levels: physical, emotional, mental, and spiritual. It's a more relaxing time because you now know each other on a deeper personal level. You are both vulnerable and are revealing sides of yourself that are not so flattering—all of your issues and insecurities. After relating to each other on a more open, honest level, you should have a common bond and trust is stronger.

The thing to be mindful of is that intimacy has a different meaning for men and women. Relationship experts have described intimacy for women is like riding a wave; emotional overload. He suggests that men should listen and be more empathetic instead of providing solutions. Intimacy for men on the other hand, is like a rubber band; get close and pull away. Give him space. The back and forth is natural for a man as his testosterone levels increases and each time he distances himself, he misses you and the connection deepens.

Getting to this stage is a milestone yet many couples get this far and don't make it to the altar. Often times it's for the best decision for both of them. Somewhere in the back of our minds we are wondering if we could be happier with someone else. Who knows? If anything love yourself first. Focus on being the best person you can be. When you are confident and comfortable with who you are, you will attract the right person. If you are on a serial dating pattern, take a break and shift your priorities to self-care. Whether it's meditation, yoga, exercise or catching up with friends, you will feel better and begin to refill. Use this time to discover more about yourself such as valuing your needs, and setting expectations and boundaries. Don't give up on finding that special person. Self-care will show you that you are worthy of love and happiness. My pastor, Craig L. Oliver says, "Ruth was noticed by Boaz when she was focused and working as hard as she had ever worked. She was successful because her focus was on seeking God, and not man." So fix your focus ladies.

"One of the greatest struggles a man faces in his life is to gather the courage to reach out to his own wife. But we touch all else, and never reach out to our own, we will die with heavy hearts and empty hands. She is generally closer than she appears."
— **Bishop T.D. Jakes**

CHAPTER 13

Marriage & Divorce

Thank goodness the stress of the dating phase is behind you. You have made it to the next stage, marital commitment. As a couple you are truly a team and believe you have a mature, sustainable love that will last until the end of time. That doesn't mean there will not be challenges and stressful situations that you have to deal with but your strong bond and effective communication should help you manage the outcomes together. Marriage takes work yet after you've gone through the other stages, it shouldn't be the hardest work you've ever done. Along with work, it takes commitment, love and respect. After all, you are both on the same page:

- You have grown accustomed to your partner's flaws and quirks

- You trust that your partner has your best interest at heart

- You envision your future together as a couple

All relationships take effort and can be complex. This definitely holds true in marriages because no other person influences your health and well-being as much as your spouse. And of course, no one knows you better than your spouse because of your daily closeness. The emotional connection and feelings you receive from your spouse cannot be filled in other social encounters.

When your marriage works you are bound to be happier and less stressed. Research suggests that married people are healthier than singles.[21] For example, when compared to singles, married couples showed more favorable health benefits such as:

- Longer life span

- Fewer strokes and heart attacks

- Lower chance of becoming depressed

- Less likely to have advanced cancer at the time of diagnosis and more likely to survive cancer for a longer period of time, and

- Survive a major operation more often

More research needs to be done in this area yet the point to take away is that this doesn't mean that being married automatically equates to good health. Married couples in stressful, unhappy marriages are likely worse off than singles who have the love and support of family and friends.

What's Love Got To Do With It

Love is patient, love is kind. It does not envy, it does not boast, it is not proud. It does not dishonor others, it is not self-seeking, it is not easily angered, it keeps no record of wrongs. Love does not delight in evil but rejoices with the truth. It always protects, always trusts, always hopes, always perseveres.

— 1 Corinthians 13:4-7

Dr. Gary Chapman created the five love languages after years of marriage counseling. Chapman believes that everyone has a primary love language that's grounded in Christian principles. Knowing our love language will help us have a healthy, happy, long-term marriage as well as other relationships. The essential ingredients are[22]:

- Love and affirmation,

- Learning how to deal with your failures through forgiveness and apology,

- Learning how to handle anger,

- Learning how to listen, and

- Accept and laugh about the minor irritations.

Then taking these five ingredients which he calls the roof and walls, he developed the foundation for the five love languages, which are the rooms inside. You don't need to go into every room but you must know which room is the most important to your spouse.

The five love languages are:

1. ***Words of affirmation*** – Saying "please" and "thank you."

2. ***Gifts*** – Shows you what the other person thinks about you. Nothing expensive. Thoughtfulness is key.

3. ***Acts of service*** – Doing things for your spouse like household chores and other things without being asked.

4. **Quality time** – Spending uninterrupted time together listening and talking creates stronger bonds. No distractions from TV, phones or computer.

5. **Physical touch** – Holding hands, kissing, sex, hugging, and playfulness.

It's a great idea for you and your spouse to take Chapman's quiz to determine your primary love language. The website information is provided in the Resources section. Knowing how to effectively communicate, please, and appreciate your spouse will add value to your marriage. After all, life is demanding and unpredictable, and when you add children, career, family, and friends into the mix, it can create a myriad of emotional and psychological challenges. Make intentional steps to keep your marriage happy and healthy and prioritize time as a couple and personal time for each one of you to recharge and refill. As long as you and your spouse are on common ground the chances of longevity are good. Put in the work for a greater return.

Divorce

Unfortunately, when things aren't clicking between the two people who were once madly in love and committed to each other, talks of divorce take center stage. I believe that all couples should at least try therapy and counseling before making the final decision to divorce. There is a real benefit to having a licensed, trained professional with evidenced based support to help you see your situation from a different perspective.

Divorce takes a toll on the couple, children, and family. Aside from the legal, financial, and emotional challenges, it takes time, energy, as well as adjusting to new schedules and responsibilities when children are involved. The stress from a divorce can take some people years to regain themselves. As with the stages of dating and marriage, there are common emotional stages couples go through when divorcing.

STAGE ONE: Blaming the Spouse

One spouse blames the other spouse for all past, present, and future problems in their life. Both spouses constantly relive scenes from the past. Often the spouse who did not initiate the divorce is angry, depressed, and has a negative self-image. This stage can be the most difficult of the emotional stages because of the changes, loss, and fear of the unknown.

STAGE TWO: Mourning the Loss

This stage is similar to the Kubler-Ross' model of the five stages of grief: i) Denial, ii) Anger; iii) Bargaining; iv) Depression and v) Acceptance.[23] Of course some people may not experience all of these stages nor in this order, but the primary focus is acknowledging the end of the relationship, and in most cases the grief feels overwhelming.

STAGE THREE: Anger and Resentment

It is a stage of rage, feeling of being betrayed, and anger from "all women" or "all men." Yet behind this anger are fears and uncertainty about the future, finances, and how to move on.

STAGE FOUR: Being Single and Deciding to Divorce

This is the acceptance stage and the feeling of freedom from no longer being a couple. You try to create an emotional distance and start dating again, trying new activities, and making your own decisions.

STAGE FIVE: New Beginnings and Acting on Decision

You are really free to make long-term plans and commitments because the marriage is dissolved. You may actually be less stressed as you see this as an improvement in your life.

At the end of the day divorce is about change. There may be a change in housing, social status, the children's lives, and your finances. All of these new changes can negatively or positively impact your health and well-being. If you are dealing with stress, anxiety, depression or trauma after your divorce, seek therapy as soon as possible in order to help you heal and become healthy. Divorce may be the end of your marriage but it is not the end of you!

"It's striking how all women are going through the same thing in different bodies and feel they are the only one going through it."
— Dr. RJ

CHAPTER 14

Hidden Trauma

A huge factor in many of my client's chronic stress levels is the result of a traumatic experience. Psychological trauma affects children and adults and it creates damage on the brain after going through it. It leaves an individual with an overwhelming feeling of distress and hopelessness that interferes with that person's ability to cope or continue life as normal.

When I first started practicing, I did not want to work with adolescents and their parents. Then I started seeing one woman after the other in similar stressful situations. Almost 80 percent of the women mentioned in this book are the type of women that I did not sign up for to work with. I can easily fall into the category of the women I see regularly. It's a thin line that is easily crossed and if you are not careful you could find yourself on the other side of the desk. I would have never chosen such outwardly successful women but they chose me. They help me as much as I help them. It is emotionally heavy but I don't feel burned out. Instead, I usually feel energized and invigorated after a day of helping.

Many women who come to see me usually believe it is for one reason and when they begin to talk, so many other things rise from the surface. Most start off with "I've never told anybody this before." My clients have a few things in common:

- well put together Black woman; picture perfect;

- not eating,

- not sleeping,

- addicted to painkillers alcohol, shopping and spending money.

She's been in this cycle for so long and does not realize why this is happening. I have had women come in for an evaluation of their child and there is something about their demeanor that tells me they could use my help.

One day a woman brought her daughter in for an evaluation. I noticed that she was impatient in the waiting room. She was aggressively pacing back and forth. I stopped what I was doing and went to the front. She was probably waiting 10 minutes max. Her daughter was suspended from school five times and she was ten years old.

"Hi, Ms. Linden. Can I speak to you for a second? I'm so sorry you had to wait. Do you have a minute for us to chat a little bit? She did not answer and followed me to my office.

"I want you to know this is a safe place for you to talk. Do you mind if I give you instructions. First take a few deep breaths and relax her body. Tell me how I can help you."

She started crying uncontrollably. I let her cry. It turns out she met a guy in prison and they were dating. When he was released he gave her an STD. She wants him to leave but he is financially providing for her and her daughter, and her nephew. She was repeatedly raped as an adult and child. She has a serious health condition and chain smokes as she believes it is the only thing she can do to calm her nerves.

This beautiful woman told me a long history of trauma. Her daughter's problems are related to her emotional instability and their chaotic environment.

"Ms. Linden I see you have a lot going on. Have you considered speaking to a therapist? All moms need to get help to talk to as it is a tough job."

"OK. I think I have to do something. I can't live like this anymore."

I helped her find a therapist and told her to check in with me once a month. Ms. Linden is a common example of a client coming in for one problem with her daughter and it turns out to be something deeper related to her unresolved issues.

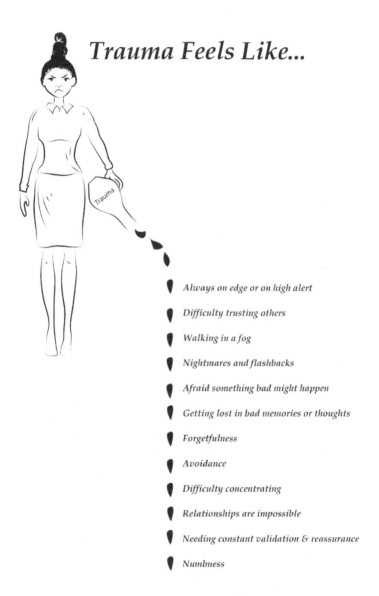

Trauma Feels Like...

Always on edge or on high alert

Difficulty trusting others

Walking in a fog

Nightmares and flashbacks

Afraid something bad might happen

Getting lost in bad memories or thoughts

Forgetfulness

Avoidance

Difficulty concentrating

Relationships are impossible

Needing constant validation & reassurance

Numbness

On average, I get 15-20 new people each week. Recently, Shirley, a woman whom I've known casually for years called me. "Hi RJ, I need to talk to you. I just had a breakdown at work and walked out. I don't trust anyone but you."

She was sitting near her new boss and had a panic attack and walked out. I told her I just wanted to do a diagnostic because it is better that I refer her to another doctor. I sent her the Adverse Childhood Experiences (ACE) Questionnaire and I asked her the following questions:

1. Tell me something that makes you comfortable.

2. Name five people you can call on if you need help and not feeling good.

Shirley had a history of depression since she was a teenager. She had gastric bypass and lost 100 pounds but gained 150 back. She really should have had therapy after her gastric bypass but no one suggested it to her. Shirley is an overeater and uses food as a drug to replace reliable relationships. In addition, she has had a lot of trauma and her ACE score is 6 out of 10.

Based on our talk, she had been with the company for 12 years and dealing with a lot of stress. She is isolated and depressed which is common and usually manifests through work. It gets covered up and the person moves from job to job because "All these people on the job are crazy!" I tell people, "wherever you go there you are." This probably happens often where people are emotionally ill and it manifests in other ways—it's their mask.

In Shirley's case, it really is her lack of tolerance of distress and she is completely empty on the inside. She has caused a scene because she cannot handle the environment being changed. I did not want to invalidate her during that initial call as it was true for her in the moment. Shirley needs to be aware that something else is going on.

Adverse Childhood Experience (ACE) Questionnaire

Please answer the following questions thinking about when you were growing up until your 18th birthday. If your answer is "Yes" please enter the number 1. In the end, you will have your total ACE Score.

1. Did a parent or other adult in the household often ...
   Swear at you, insult you, put you down, or humiliate you?
   or
   Act in a way that made you afraid that you might be physically hurt?
   Yes No Yes: _____

2. Did a parent or other adult in the household often...
   Push, grab, slap, or throw something at you?
   or
   Ever hit you so hard that you had marks or were injured?
   Yes No   Yes: _____

3. Did an adult or person at least 5 years older than you ever...
   Touch or fondle you or have you touch their body in a sexual way?
   or
   Try to or actually have oral, anal, or vaginal sex with you?
   Yes No   Yes: _____

4. Did you often feel that...
   No one in your family loved you or thought you were important or special?
   or
   Your family didn't look out for each other, feel close to each other, or support each other?
   Yes No   Yes: _____

5. Did you often feel that...
   You didn't have enough to eat, had to wear dirty clothes, and had no one to protect you?   or
   Your parents were too high or drunk to take care of you or take you to the doctor if you needed it?
                                   Yes No Yes: _____

ACE Questionnaire Continued...
6. Were your parents ever separated or divorced?
   Yes No   Yes: _____

7. Was your mother or stepmother:
   Often pushed, grabbed, slapped, or had something thrown at her?
   or
   Sometimes or often kicked, bitten, hit with a fist, or hit with something hard?
   or
   Ever repeatedly hit over at least a few minutes or threatened with a gun or knife?
   Yes No Yes: _____

8. Did you live with anyone who was a problem drinker or alcoholic or who used street drugs?
   Yes No Yes: _____

9. Was a household member depressed or mentally ill or did a household member attempt suicide?
   Yes No Yes: _____

10. Did a household member go to prison?
    Yes No   Yes: _____

All of your "Yes" answers is your ACE Score: _____

Adverse Childhood Experiences International Questionnaire (ACE-IQ)".
World Health Organization. Retrieved 29 March 2014

How to Refill Your Empty Vessel
TRAUMA

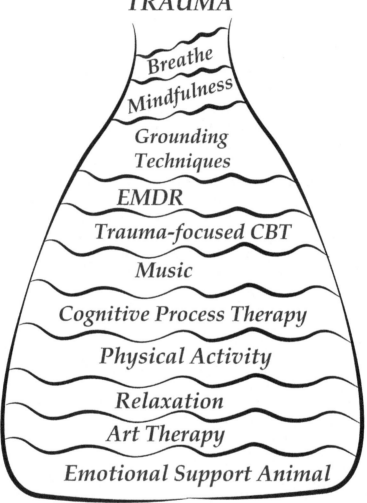

Breathe

Mindfulness

Grounding Techniques

EMDR

Trauma-focused CBT

Music

Cognitive Process Therapy

Physical Activity

Relaxation

Art Therapy

Emotional Support Animal

"Anxiety and depression are like first cousins in the brain."
— Dr. RJ

CHAPTER 15

Anxiety

A nxiety disorders are a serious psychiatric disorder that involves extreme worry or fear. These disorders are the most common mental disorders in the United States, and an estimated 264 million people worldwide have an anxiety disorder.[24] Women are disproportionately affected by anxiety with nearly twice as high diagnoses than men. However, research demonstrates that Black women experience anxiety disorders more chronic and intense than our white counterparts.[25] Part of the problem may come from the societal portrayals of black women which we touched upon in the previous "Lies" section: (i) Black women are angry, and (ii) Black women are sexually advanced. These negative stereotypes affect how we view ourselves which heightens our social anxiety because we are constantly under a microscope in settings where we are out to prove ourselves or compete—whether academic or the workplace.

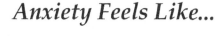

Anxiety Feels Like...

- *Constant worry & fear*
- *Unable to relax*
- *Constantly on edge*
- *Mind & body on high alert for no reason*
- *Pretending you're OK but really you can't breathe or think straight*
- *Your mind is racing and you have so many thoughts at the same time that it is hard to have one complete thought*
- *Needing to escape but not being able to*
- *Everything happening all at once*
- *Upset stomach or queasy*

There are several types of anxiety disorders and I will discuss those most common.

- ***Generalized anxiety disorder (GAD)*** - Is exhibited when a person is excessively worried about a variety of things like money, health, work, or other issues. They constantly worry about disasters and things beyond their control. Without medication and treatment, GAD individuals are not able to control their worry. This type of anxiety disorder comes on gradually with the highest risk between childhood and middle age. Biological factors such as family background and stressful life experiences contribute to those diagnosed with GAD.

- ***Panic disorder and panic attacks*** - Occurs when a person has a sudden panic attack and become preoccupied with fear that the attack will happen again. Panic disorder usually begins after age 21 and can cause a major disruption in a person's life as they avoid situations for fear of having another attack. People diagnosed with panic disorder call out sick more often and over schedule on doctor's visits to the point where people close to them may label them as hypochondriacs.

- ***Social anxiety disorder (social phobia)*** - This is the second most commonly diagnosed disorder affecting nearly 15 million Americans as the result of a specific phobia.[26] People diagnosed with social phobia have exhibit extreme anxiety or fear at being judged, evaluated or rejected during a social or performance situation. Therefore, making presentations at work or other settings can be stressful as they are worried about their physical appearance as well as every aspect of their delivery. In addition, individuals experience physical symptoms such as sweating, rapid heart beat, and nausea. Research demonstrates that people living with this fear tend to be more prone to depression and alcohol abuse. For the most part, women diagnosed with social phobia tend to avoid social performance environments in general.

Over the years, I've treated numerous clients for GAD and social phobias. Geneva sticks out in my mind because she was the epitome of a cover girl—fabulous on the outside but fragile and empty on the inside. Her first husband was a high powered Wall Street executive. Heads turned when he entered a room with his tall, dark, and handsome physique. He and Geneva only dated for a short while and it wasn't until the honeymoon that he confessed that he was gay. She was devastated and got pregnant on that honeymoon weekend and later gave birth to a son. Her husband filed for divorce on their son's first birthday.

As I have mentioned, many forms of mental illness are linked genetically and more often than not the person experienced some type of trauma or life-changing event during childhood. In Geneva's case, we can look to her parents. Her mom is a tall dark-skinned woman. Her dad was biracial; Black and Portugese. Geneva describes herself as a "Mixed Chick" and swears by their product line. Throughout her life Geneva's mom belittled her, failed to hug or kiss her, and chastised her about her looks, with these types of harsh words, "You're not that cute. Don't let your light-skin go to your head. If it's one thing you will never hear me say to you is that you are beautiful or cute!"

Geneva heard these negative words spoken over her by her mother since elementary school. Her mother's comments always made her feel inferior. She was a "daddy's girl" yet her dad died when she was a teenager. Each time she had a project due at school such as a book report or science fair presentation she wet the bed the night before and was often excused from presenting at school because she had a headache, was nauseous, and once she threw up on a classmate. Geneva's inferiority complex has had a long-term effect on her health and the health of her son who is currently on a high dosage of ADHD medication. She excels in her career and during her last year end bonus, her salary was near a half million dollars. However, she is extremely anxious and worried every single night whether she will meet her target sales goals, and what the client thought of her presentation and outfit.

She showers friends with lavish gifts and volunteers to host every sorority party at her home spending thousands of dollars unnecessarily as she fears something will go wrong with the party so she makes sure every base is covered at least double. In addition, she constantly shops for groceries for fear that she will run out of food even though she has two refrigerators upstairs and two freezers in the basement that are overflowing with food. Her pantry is bursting at the seams and there is food stockpiled in the garage. Geneva went through counseling, was on medication, and also incorporated yoga and guided meditation into her self-care routine. She is not completely healed, but she is definitely a better version of her old self.

There are several additional anxiety disorders and phobias that you should be aware of. More information is provided in the Resources section. If you have been experiencing prolonged periods of excessive fear and worry about managing daily life functions, talk to your primary care physician who can refer you to a mental health professional once physical disorders are ruled out. Anxiety disorders are treatable and can help you get on track towards implementing new routines in your life to refill your empty vessel.

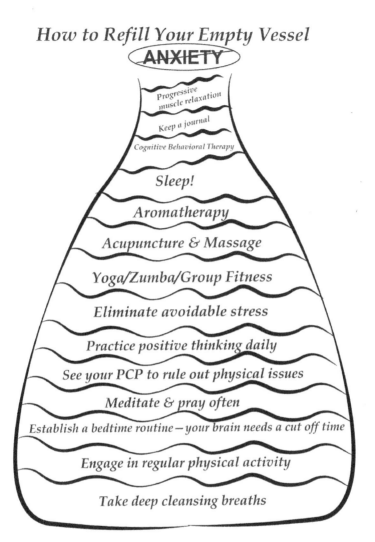

How to Refill Your Empty Vessel

ANXIETY

Progressive muscle relaxation

Keep a journal

Cognitive Behavioral Therapy

Sleep!

Aromatherapy

Acupuncture & Massage

Yoga/Zumba/Group Fitness

Eliminate avoidable stress

Practice positive thinking daily

See your PCP to rule out physical issues

Meditate & pray often

Establish a bedtime routine – your brain needs a cut off time

Engage in regular physical activity

Take deep cleansing breaths

"This might sound simple, but I cannot overstate this: The single most important thing is recognizing what the problem is in the first place."
— Dr. Nadine Burke Harris

CHAPTER 16

Depression

Mental illness does not discriminate. People of all ages and all racial, ethnic and socioeconomic backgrounds experience depression. Depression is a serious mental health condition that affects more women than men because of our biological, hormonal, and social differences that specifically affect us. For those on the outside looking in and don't understand depression, it's not just feeling sad, going through a rough patch or something that you can instantly "snap out of." Depression requires immediate medical care by a licensed professional. If left untreated, depression can be devastating for those individuals suffering with it as well as their families.

Research demonstrates that there are contributing causes to depression as opposed to one single factor. Depression can come about as a result of trauma or a life changing event. In addition, depression is genetically linked, so it is important to know family history. Of course this becomes challenging as discussions around mental illness are uncomfortable and stigmatized in the Black community. Therefore many generations suffer from depression and are never treated. When I ask my clients about family history of mental illness, usually the answer is inconclusive or "I think my mom was depressed but no one every said anything."

From a biological perspective, brain scans of individuals diagnosed with depression shows that the frontal lobe of the brain is less active. This is an important fact because our frontal lobe controls a variety of key behaviors such as our executive functions, problem-solving, memory, language, spontaneity, judgment, impulse control, as well as social and sexual behavior.

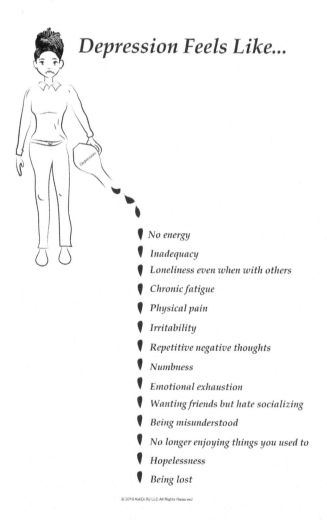

Depression Feels Like...

No energy

Inadequacy

Loneliness even when with others

Chronic fatigue

Physical pain

Irritability

Repetitive negative thoughts

Numbness

Emotional exhaustion

Wanting friends but hate socializing

Being misunderstood

No longer enjoying things you used to

Hopelessness

Being lost

The good news is that with early detection, diagnosis and a treatment plan taking into account a combination of medication, psychotherapy, and lifestyle choices, most people with depression get better and live happier. Individuals may have only one episode in a lifetime, but for most people suffering with this mental illness, depression recurs. If left untreated, episodes can last from a few months to several years. "There is an estimated 16 million American adults—almost 7% of the population claimed to have had at least one major depressive episode in the past year."[27]

Although there are studies indicating that depression affects women more than men, there are additional studies which found that men don't report symptoms as much and practitioners may not suspect irritability and insomnia as symptoms of depression in men. Women experience powerful physical and hormonal changes throughout their lives. Specifically, during our menstrual cycle, pregnancy, the postpartum period, and perimenopause, are all biological stages where depression can impact a woman's life. It is important to be aware of what's happening to your body during the following phases:

Premenstrual Dysphoric Disorder (PMDD)

PMDD is a more serious form of our commonly known PMS or premenstrual syndrome. We are all too familiar with moodiness and irritability prior to and during our menstrual cycle. However, women experiencing PMDD episodes are dealing with more disabling symptoms in addition to moodiness and irritability, such as anger, feeling depressed, sadness, suicidal thoughts, appetite changes, bloating, tenderness in the breast area and joint or muscle pain.

Perinatal Depression

In addition to morning sickness, weight gain and mood swings during pregnancy, many new moms experience what's called "the baby blues" where they go through feelings of worry, unhappiness, mood swings, and fatigue. These types of feelings should not last long and should dissipate once new mom's adjust to their baby. Conversely, after the baby is born and moms fail to make the mental adjustments, that's where a more serious condition called perinatal depression or depression during or after (postpartum) pregnancy occurs. Not only are new moms going through the baby-blues symptoms but perinatal depression hinders a mom's ability to function daily and care for herself and her baby.

Perimenopausal Depression

Transitioning into menopause is a normal phase in a woman's life. Women diagnosed with perimenopausal depression may experience abnormal periods, problems sleeping, mood swings, and hot flashes. The most important thing to note about this stage is that it's "not normal" to feel depressed, which many people believe is the case. Women struggling with perimenopausal depression may have symptoms of anxiety, irritability, sadness or feel "down in the dumps" often.

Persistent Depressive Disorder (Dysthymia)

When a person is diagnosed with persistent depressive disorder, also called dysthymia, they have a chronic form of depression that has been continuous for at least two years, and may last a lifetime. Symptoms may include losing interest in normal daily activities, feeling hopeless, lack productivity, tiredness and fatigue, trouble concentrating and making decisions, low self-esteem and feelings of inadequacy. These feelings may significantly interfere with relationships, career and daily activities.

Although this form of depressive disorder is not as severe as major depression may be mild, moderate or severe as intensity can change over time. Psychotherapy and medication have been effective in treating this condition.

Bipolar Disorder

Bipolar disorder is a lifelong condition. It is also referred to as manic-depressive illness, which is a brain disorder that causes unusual shifts in mood, energy, activity levels, and the ability to carry out daily tasks. People with bipolar disorder experience mood changes that are extremely "high and elated" or extremely "low and sad" with periods of hopelessness known as depressive episodes.

Those diagnosed with bipolar disorder also go through "mood episodes" of intense emotional changes in sleep patterns, activity levels, and unusual behaviors. It's also likely that people with bipolar disorder have another mental illness such as anxiety, substance abuse or an eating disorder which puts them at higher risk for thyroid disease, migraines, heart disease, diabetes, obesity and other physical illnesses.

There are four types of bipolar disorders: i) Bipolar I - severe mood episodes from mania to depression; ii) Bipolar II - milder mood elevations of hypomania (elevated energy level, not normal, but not to the point of mania) that fluctuate with periods of depression; iii) Cyclothymic - alternating brief periods of hypomania and depression; and iv) Mixed features - simultaneous symptoms of opposite mood swings during the other three episodes: manic, hypomania and depression. Treatment for bipolar disorder is focused on managing the symptoms including medication such as mood stabilizers, psychotherapy and other treatment options.

Depression Diagnosis

Women diagnosed with depression have experienced a major depressive episode that has lasted longer than two weeks. Depression is treatable, so make an effort to seek professional help. Treatments can include medication and other forms of psychotherapy.[28]

Depression Tips

- Research suggests that mild to moderate depression responds best to psychotherapy, particularly CBT (Cognitive Behavior Therapy) and stress reduction.

- Moderate to severe depression or depression in a person who has a family history of depression responds best to CBT and medication.

- Medication for anxiety is not effective as a long-term treatment.

- No one treatment will work alone. Our minds, bodies, and spirits all require regular attention and function better when we care for them as a whole.

How to Refill Your Empty Vessel
DEPRESSION

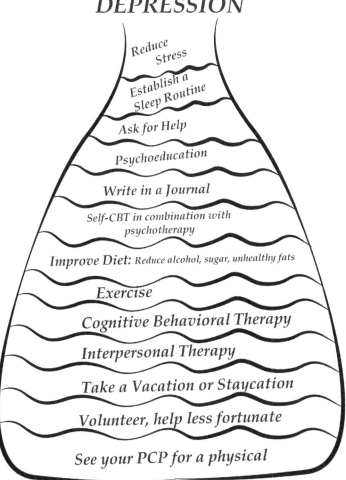

Reduce Stress

Establish a Sleep Routine

Ask for Help

Psychoeducation

Write in a Journal

Self-CBT in combination with psychotherapy

Improve Diet: Reduce alcohol, sugar, unhealthy fats

Exercise

Cognitive Behavioral Therapy

Interpersonal Therapy

Take a Vacation or Staycation

Volunteer, help less fortunate

See your PCP for a physical

"Pain is temporary. It gives us information about ourselves. But suffering, suffering is unnatural."
— **Dr. RJ**

CHAPTER 17

Suicide

Every suicide is a tragedy. Although the cause of suicide is unknown, the most prominent linkage is depression. Suicide is a complex and multifaceted severe form of human behavior. Factors such as personal and family history, neurobiology (structure and function of the nervous system), stress-related events, and sociocultural experiences are all interrelated to this unfortunate outcome.

When someone is experiencing severe or long-term stress it can become overwhelming. Functioning in a continuous cycle of stress, anxiety, trauma or depression may leave you with deep feelings of hopelessness. These negative emotions hinder your ability to see solutions to your problems and you believe that the only remedy is to take your own life.

Careful attention must be paid to those with suicidal ideation. Whether active or passive, suicidal ideation must be taken seriously. It's when a person's mind is in a dark place and replays thoughts of their ultimate death. Active ideation is when a person has decided they want to die and has considered the method to do so. Conversely, passive ideation can take the form of envisioning dying in your sleep, an automobile accident, or terminal illness. Either of these thoughts of death need to be addressed immediately.

Equally important are those who attempt suicide. Oftentimes people attempt suicide as a cry for help, not so much because they really want to die. Suicide attempts tells the world, "I am in pain, I am hurting, I need to escape the pain, and I need someone to hear me and help me deal with this devastating emotion." Individuals who make failed attempts are at a much higher risk of trying again. Unfortunately, their second attempts more than likely prove tragic. However, with professional therapy, those who have attempted suicide can go on to live healthy, fulfilled lives. Suicide is the 4th leading cause of death for adults 18 to 65.[29] Suicide rates for females are the highest amont those aged 45-54. Women are more likely than men to attempt suicide, yet men are more likely than women to complete suicide.

A final behavior or symptom to be mindful of when a person withdraws from normal activities is social isolation. A person can become socially isolated for a number of reasons, including losing friends, a job or a spouse, separation or divorce, physical or mental illness, social anxiety, retirement, or moving to a new location. One cause for social isolation may be low self-esteem which can lead to loneliness or other risk factors such as suicidial ideation, depression and alcohol or drug misuse.

A Cry For Help

Celeste is a 42-year-old strikingly beautiful woman with a successful six-figure career as a counselor. She has had significant trauma throughout her teenage years, has suicidal ideations, and frequent panic attacks. She has been married for several years to a man she does not love because he is safe for her. Celeste grew up in a prominent community on the West Coast where her father was a well-known politician. Her family is well respected in the community. She is the middle child of an older brother and younger brother.

Her father worked constantly and her mother was a stay at home mom. Celeste's "daddy issues" stemmed from her father being extremely judgmental. She could never understand how he did a thousand and one things for the community and was absent at home. She felt like she was never good enough for her father nor could she do anything to gain his love and appreciation.

The family were devoutly religious and did not believe in therapy. Celeste was raped in high school but never told anyone because of her father's stature in the community. She ran away from home several times hoping that someone would come and rescue her but no one ever came. Her parents believed in tough love.

As a result of searching for love, she got into a lot of abusive relationships. She became a stripper and went down a path of living a dangerous life in her teens. Celeste had three children before turning 21. She moved from city-to-city including New York, Las Vegas, Florida, and Philadelphia. Due to her dangerous lifestyle, she contracted HIV. She also started using cocaine.

Despite her outward appearance, Celeste is drowning on the inside because her mental illness had gone untreated for many years. She is not accepted by her family nor her community and it has now shortened her life. Even though she is stable, she continues to have panic attacks and suicidal ideation. Celeste is fragile; like a glass vase with cracks and broken pieces on the inside. On the outside she comes from an affluent family with a great husband, yet thinks about ending her life all the time.

Women like Celeste need to be in therapy. They need a psychological, spiritual, and holistic approach to their well-being. Their inner-child needs to be healed. The emotional void from a present but absent father created an atmosphere of devastating loss that was overlooked during childhood. Women with Celeste's symptoms and experiences may also have an untreated bipolar disorder. There are so many beautiful, successful, women of color like Celeste who think about dying every day. We have to stand in the gap for each other. Talk to your girlfriend. Talk to your sister. Talk to your doctor. Seek professional therapy. Our sister's are crying for help and they need us.

SUICIDAL WARNING SIGNS

Emotional: "Feeling"

- feeling depressed
- lack of interest in activities once enjoyed
- irritability
- anger
- anxiety
- shame or humiliation
- mood swings

Verbal: "Talking about"

- killing themselves
- their life having no purpose
- feeling like a burden
- feeling stuck
- not wanting to exist

Behavioral: "Doing"

- isolating from others
- not communicating with friends or family
- giving away possessions or writing a will
- driving recklessly
- increased aggression
- increased drug and alcohol use
- searching about suicide on the internet
- gathering materials (pills or a weapon)

I'M EXPERIENCING THOUGHTS OF SUICIDE

 Contact the National Suicide Prevention Life Line: **1-800-273-8255**. They also have an online chat and text. Text **"Home" to 741-741**.

Know that you aren't alone. You aren't crazy, weak, or flawed.

You have more pain than you can cope with right now, and although it feels overwhelming and permanent, with time and support, the pain and suicidal feelings will pass.

Your emotions are not fixed. Pain is temporary.

Depression has a way of tricking the brain into thinking that nothing will ever get better.

Avoid being alone.

Tell someone.

How to cope if you've lost a friend or loved one to suicide:

1. *Accept how you're feeling:* Your emotions are valid and will vary throughout your healing process. You may feel shock, guilt, anger, shame, denial, anxiety, confusion, loneliness and in some cases relief.

2. *There's no timeline:* Don't worry about when you should stop feeling negative emotions or how long you are grieving. Everyone's path will be different. Focus on your needs and what you can do to heal and move forward.

3. *Self-care:* You cannot heal if you are depleted. Do your best to eat properly, get adequate sleep, exercise, yoga, meditation or pick up a relaxing hobby.

4. *Stay connected:* Talk to and accept help from those who have been support to you in the past, whether family, friends, church or other connections.

5. *Talk to a professional:* A psychologist and other mental health professionals can help you express and manage your feelings as well as provide coping strategies, resources and tools.

"Out of suffering has emerged the strongest souls; The most massive characters are seared with scars.
— **Khalil Gibran**

CHAPTER 18

Why Therapy?

I t is unfortunate that stigma and shame has prevented many Black people from seeking help from a licensed therapist. Therapy is not "paying someone just to talk." It is a scientifically-proven process that not only teaches you about the inner workings of your mind, but it also helps you manage your emotions, reconstruct better behaviors and manage your thoughts in a healthier way so you can live happier and balanced. Many therapists use Cognitive Behavioral Therapy (CBT) which helps you set goals, track progress, and measure results. CBT helps you build emotional resilience so that you can end therapy and manage on your own. Take control of your life and try therapy. It's definitely a priceless investment in your overall self-care and wellness routine.

You'd be surprised by the things people say to me about why they choose not to engage in therapy:

- "What happens in my house stays in my house, I wasn't raised to be telling all my business!"

- "Some stuff you just need to figure out on your own."

- "Therapy is for crazy, rich, white, weak people."

- "I can't afford it."

- "I don't have time."
- "There's nothing wrong with me."
- "I don't see how talking about something over and over will help."
- "I just pray and fast."
- "My pastor said that depression is a sin."
- "I tried it once and it just made me feel worse."
- "Talking about all that stuff made me feel worse, it was better when I pretended nothing happened."
- "I'm not paying people to listen to my problems."

So many people regardless of ethnicity feel the same way but these responses are really not true. These common misconceptions prevent people from making positive, life-changing benefits for themselves and others around them. Although the importance of mental health awareness is trending on social media, more needs to be done to provide accurate information on the advantages engaging in therapy and types or forms of therapy. Regardless of whether you believe you have a big issue or small issue, a therapist can help. All it takes is for one person to have a bad experience and then all therapeutic approaches are painted with a negative brushstroke. Over the years, scientific studies consistently show that cognitive and behavioral interventions can be just as effective as medication for mild to moderate issues.

Of course, sometimes, you can work out issues on your own by exercising, making changes to your environment, friends, lifestyle, reading self-help books and attending conferences. Yet there are life's challenges that can come at you so quickly that cause stress and anxiety which can wreak havoc on your body. In those instances, you should talk to a professional to help you learn more about yourself to get better. It is truly a "safe space" to speak freely and process your emotions. It is important to recognize that therapy should always have a goal and once your goals have been met you should be able to manage and live a healthy life on your own. If you feel old habits returning, don't hesitate to schedule a "tune-up" with your therapist.

HOW TO CHOOSE A THERAPIST

1) Ask friends and family for referrals.
2) Research online: psychologytoday.com and review photos and profiles.
Therapyforblackgirls.com is a national network of culturally informed therapists.
3) Be sure that your therapist is licensed in your state.
4) Find a therapist who specializes in your area of concern.
5) Ask if your therapist has a therapist or has been in therapy. I personally would not want a therapist who hasn't been in therapy before.
6) Interview your therapist. Most therapists allow a brief complimentary phone consultation.
7) Hang in there. Don't give up after a few sessions. However, if your therapist truly isn't a good fit, let her know and ask for a referral.

FAQs IS MEDICATION FOR ME?

People of color often have a cultural mistrust of medicine, doctors, psychologists, and social workers for valid reasons. Historically, systematic racism has contributed to deadly experimentation like the Tuskegee Syphilis Study, misdiagnosis of learning and behavioral disorders, separation of families (foster care) and a number of other injustices. However, complete mistrust can lead to ineffective treatment and unnecessary suffering.

Below are a few guidelines to help you make an informed decision. The best treatment includes collaboration between you, your primary care physician, your therapist, and a psychologist.

 Share your symptoms with all of your providers. I often find that my patients have shared symptoms with me that their PCP is unaware of, such as insomnia or gastrointestinal issues.

 Get an updated physical often. Hormonal imbalances, thyroid issues or other medical conditions come with anxiety and depression symptoms.

 SLEEP! Lack of sleep wreaks havoc on the brain and the body.

 Eliminate avoidable stress and add "relaxation" to your to do list.

 Manage your response to stressors. Chronic stress can kill!

Improve your diet. Excessive sugar, fatty foods, processed foods, and junk food can alter your mood and energy level.

 Do your own research. Use reputable resources and ask questions.

 Build a relationship with your practitioners. You are the expert of you and we are on your team.

 Remember that medication is not a cure. It treats symptoms. Wellness is achieved by a daily and consistent routine of self-care. The mind, body, and spirit must all be healthy in order to achieve wellness.

"Self-care is not selfish. You can't serve from an empty vessel."
— Dr. RJ

CHAPTER 19

Can I Get A Refill?

Self-care is a vital, life-sustaining need. As women, we must be careful not to put it on the back burner as something to do in the future. Prioritizing self-care gives your body a chance to recuperate from the negative stress cycle that impacts you daily. You should never be "too busy" for self-care. When you neglect self-care you are increasing the negative short and long-term effects on your mind and body; stress, trauma, anxiety, depression, and other mental health disorders create physical damage to the body in the long run. Pay attention to these side effects that impact your body when you continue to operate on empty:

- Feelings of fatigue or insomnia
- Feelings of inadequacy
- Blaming others
- Initiating arguments, easily irritated
- Having poor relationships
- Experiencing brain fog, confused, forgetful, difficulty focusing
- Gaining weight

With competing demands for our time and attention at home, work, and other activities, there is only a limited time in a day to get things done. We all have the same 24 hours in a day, and eight of those hours should be spent sleeping. How you spend your time is important. I recommend using social media moderately and sparingly when you are well and if you are in treatment, take a break from it. Be careful of what you spend your time and energy reading. For example, if you find yourself feeling upset and arguing with strangers on random posts, realize that is valuable time subtracted from self-care.

Although social media can be a positive source for many things, it can also be triggering in instances of anxiety, depression, trauma, feelings of inadequacy or low self esteem. Social media is best used for entertainment, desired long distance connections, and exchanging resources and information. When social media is used to follow other people's lives, especially in times of dissatisfaction with your own, it can trigger an unhealthy connection and even an obsession with other people's highlight reels. Social media in itself isn't a negative thing but we must examine our inner selves and be mindful of what we consume. The eyes are the gateway to the heart.

Why is it so hard to practice self-care? I think it's because we are so wired to get things done that we operate in "go mode" so much that we get stuck. We literally have to train our bodies to stop, breathe, take a break, and engage in self-care remedies to recharge and refill. This may look like a self-care "To-Do List." Even if you can't get away make time throughout your day to:

- Stop & smell the roses...be present and take in all the sights, sounds and smells around you;

- Go for a walk and breathe in fresh air;

- Write in your journal;

- Be creative by drawing, coloring or crafting;

- Meditate or listen to soothing music or ocean sounds; or

- Connect with a friend for lunch or dinner.

We are carrying too much stress and hurting on the inside. It's really OK to take off the mask, cape, and red bottom shoes. Take a break and listen to your body. I like to think of our minds and bodies as a smartphone. At some point, an over-charged battery stops working at 100% and even when charged, it still doesn't work as good. It's the same with a lack of self-care. You get to a place where you're giving your all but it's still not enough. Only when you fully replace your battery and create new habits will you have the ability to meet your fullest potential. Bootleg chargers (temporary fixes) won't work—get some real help. You deserve it. It's time to recharge, replenish, and refill. No more stress. No more lies. No more vacancy. Be well.

Dr. Raushannah Johnson-Verwayne, also known as "Dr. RJ" is a licensed clinical psychologist and the founder of Standard of Care Psychological Services, LLC, in Atlanta, GA. Dr. RJ brings a balance of science, practicality, wit, humor, and relatedness. Whether it's speaking at a women's conference, hosting a corporate retreat, or attending a grassroots community service event in the community, Dr. RJ is passionate about wellness and self-care.

She advocates for those affected by emotional and behavioral issues and focuses on evidence-based, trauma-informed care, to improve the overall quality of life for clients. With many years of experience, Dr. RJ has mastered helping clients develop realistic, long-lasting, and life-changing goals.

Dr. RJ attended North Carolina A&T State University where she earned her bachelor's degree in psychology, graduating with highest honors. Dr. RJ also became a member of Alpha Kappa Alpha Sorority, Incorporated while matriculating through NC A&T. After graduating she went on to earn her masters and doctorate degrees in clinical psychology from the Georgia School of Professional Psychology. Dr. RJ has a special interest in treating trauma in victims of child sex trafficking and has partnered with two local Senators to eradicate this widespread atrocity. Dr. RJ was awarded a grant from the Fulton Dekalb Hospital Authority in order to prevent child sex trafficking at the primary level of intervention. In 2015, Dr. RJ was appointed by Chairman John Eaves of the Fulton County Board of Commissioners to play an integral role on a task force to end the Commercial Sexual Exploitation of Children. The task force has had monumental success and was applauded during a publicly broadcasted board meeting by the Board of Commissioners for their work. Dr. RJ has continued with the task force under the leadership of Chairman Rob Pitts. In addition, Dr. RJ was appointed to represent Fulton County Region 3 as an Advisory Council member to the Department of Behavioral Health and Developmental Disabilities.

Dr. RJ is known for her service in the community. She has served on a panel moderated by former Atlanta Mayor Shirley Franklin on the topic of child sex trafficking, appeared as a presenter to train over 100 Gwinnett County school counselors and educators about childhood trauma, served as a co-moderator with Senator Donzella James to discuss Amendment 1 (Opportunity School District), and served as the keynote speaker on a program for Domestic Violence Awareness and Prevention. Dr. RJ has been <u>featured as an expert</u> on the documentaries Killer Kids on the Lifetime Movie Network and For My Man on TV One. Dr. RJ also serves as the Wellness Wednesday expert for the Kansas City radio station KPRS 103 Jamz! She has received numerous community awards including the Atlanta magazine Woman of Power and Influence, the 100 Black Women Mecca chapter Honoree for commitment to Health and Wellness, the Higher Standard Superstar award from People You Need to Know magazine, and many other community mentions. Dr. RJ has also served as the keynote speaker for several mental health and wellness conferences. She is an active member of Elizabeth Baptist Church and the Tau Epsilon Omega Chapter of Alpha Kappa Alpha Sorority, Inc. Dr. RJ is also a certified Zumba instructor and is passionate about teaching the importance of the mind, body, spirit connection as it relates to total wellness.

As an African-American woman, Dr. RJ recognizes the unique impact of stress on her demographic. Author of the newly published book *Stress, Lies and Vacancy: Self Care to Refill Your Empty Vessel,* Dr. RJ's experiences and transparency provide an empowering self-help guide for women of color to reduce common stressors in their lives that have long term effects on the body and brain. Through this latest endeavor, Dr. RJ is on a mission to heal one woman at a time and debunk the myth of the Black superwoman. Although she absolutely loves her career, her ultimate joy comes from her faith in God, and her love for her husband and their two children. Dr. RJ's favorite quote is "Self-care isn't selfish. You can't serve from an empty vessel".

Resources

Find a Therapist Near You

- Psychologytoday.com

- Therapyforblackgirls.com

Helplines

- National Suicide Prevention Helpline 1-800-273-8255

- National Domestic Violence Hotline | Get Help Today | 1-800-799-7233

- National Alliance on Mental Illness (NAMI) 1-800-950-NAMI

- National Institute of Mental Health (NIMH) 1-800-273-825

Mental Health Organizations

- American Psychological Association (APA) www.APA.org

- Anxiety and Depression Association of America (ADAA) https://adaa.org/find-help-for/women/anxiety

- National Institute of Mental Health (NIMH) https://www.nimh.nih.gov/health/topics/index.shtml

- Blackdoctor.org: https://blackdoctor.org/category/healthy-living/womens-health/

Relationships, Family & Finances

Dr. Gary Chapman: The Five Love Languages - https://www.5lovelanguages.com/

Black and Married With Kids: https://blackandmarriedwithkids.com/

Dave Ramsey Financial Tools: https://www.daveramsey.com/blog/a-financial-plan-that-works

Mental Health & Wellness Videos

Dr. Nadine Harris Burke (TED Talk) - How Childhood Trauma Affects Health Across a Lifetime:

https://www.ted.com/talks/nadine_burke_harris_how_childhood_trauma_affects_health_across_a_lifetime?utm_source=tedcomshare&utm_medium=email&utm_campaign=tedspread

**For Bookings &
More Information
Visit: www.
askdrrj.com**

Endnotes

1. Dias, Brian G., Ressler, Kerry, J., "Parental olfactory experiences influences behavior and neural structure in subsequent generations, Nature Neuroscience, 17.89 (2013) online.

2. https://www.huffpost.com/entry/85-of-what-we-worry-about_b_8028368

3. Hanson, Rick. *Hardwiring Happiness: The New Brain Science of Contentment, Calm, and Confidence.* Unabridged ed. [Melbourne, Vic.]: Bolinda audio, 2014.

4. https://www.webmd.com/balance/news/20110916/optimism-partly-in-your-genes#1

5. https://madamenoire.com/1026019/the-strained-relationship-between-black-mothers-and-their-daughters/

6. https://www.afro.com/census-bureau-higher-percentage-black-children-live-single-mothers/

7. https://ifstudies.org/blog/how-instability-affects-kids

8. https://www.youtube.com/watch?v=Ea8pHeetkgo

9.lifewayresearch.com/2013/09/17/mental-health-half-of-evangelicals-believe-prayer-can-heal-mental-illness/

10. Colossians 4:14

11. 1 Kings 17-19, 1 Kings 21:11-29, 2 Kings 1:1-2, 18, Luke 4:25-26, James 5:17-18

12. https://www.joydegruy.com/post-traumatic-slave-syndrome

13. https://www.joydegruy.com/post-traumatic-slave-syndrome

14.https://www.psychologicalscience.org/news/releases/faces-of-black-children-as-young-as-five-evoke-negative-biases.html

15. https://www.apa.org/news/press/releases/2014/03/black-boys-older

16.https://www.law.georgetown.edu/news/black-girls-viewed-as-less-innocent-than-white-girls-georgetown-law-research-finds-2/

17. Ibid

18.https://www.usatoday.com/story/news/2016/06/07/black-students-nearly-4x-likely-suspended/85526458/

19. https://www.sahistory.org.za/people/sara-saartjie-baartman

20.https://www.heart.org/idc/groups/ahamah-public/@wcm/@sop/@smd/documents/downloadable/ucm_480110.pdf

21. https://www.health.harvard.edu/blog/the-health-advantages-of-marriage-2016113010667

22. Chapman, Gary D. 1995. *The Five Love Languages: How to Express Heartfelt Commitment to Your Mate.*

23. https://www.psycom.net/depression.central.grief.html

24. https://adaa.org/find-help-for/women/anxiety

25. https://adaa.org/learn-from-us/from-the-experts/blog-posts/consumer/be-female-anxious-and-black

26. https://adaa.org/understanding-anxiety/social-anxiety-disorder

27. https://www.nami.org/Learn-More/Mental-Health-Conditions/Depression

28. Ibid

29. https://www.cdc.gov/vitalsigns/suicide/index.html

30. https://www.edrawsoft.com/genogram/how-to-create-genogram.php

Made in the USA
Columbia, SC
18 January 2023

75546422R00114